Improve your Wordpower

Rosalind Birley

Hugos's Language Books Ltd, London

Set in 11/13 Plantin by
Typesetters Ltd
Printed and bound in Great Britain by
Hollen Street Press Ltd

Contents

Preface

Good verbal skills are important whatever you do. A command of language and a wide vocabulary make self-presentation and clear writing much easier. Like all skills, an ability with words is something which must be learnt, and not given at birth. Verbal ability comes from developing good habits and practice as much as any other skill, like playing an instrument or learning a foreign language.

Words are not only functional, however. They are mental stimulants and food for the imagination too. A number of exercises in this book may have no direct effect on your verbal skills, but are intended to test your sensitivity to and inventiveness with words. These qualities are not of course irrelevant to verbal skills; it would be difficult not to have a good command of language without being aware of the qualities associated with words, or without having any capacity for using words creatively.

Other exercises are aimed at increasing range of vocabulary and precision with words. Using words imprecisely and inaccurately makes for poor communication; only when words are used with their correct, specific meaning are they really effective. The larger your vocabulary, the easier it is to be specific – because you have a greater choice of words to use.

There are as many ways not to improve your wordpower as there are ways to strengthen it. Using meaningless phrases and clichés are the most common and insidious means of reducing your vocabulary. You will find practice in correcting these bad habits towards the end of the book. So if, *at this moment in time* you incline towards these phrases, let's hope that *at the end of the day* you'll be dissuaded from using them!

Introduction

The exercises in this book will be useful to many different people: for the student taking exams who wishes to improve his verbal adroitness; for the foreigner who wishes to better his already fluent level of English; and for the professional who realizes he must improve his articulacy to further his career. It will also appeal to those who enjoy word games as testing mental exercises. Most of the exercises number ten questions each and are of mixed difficulty throughout. Sample questions and answers to all the exercises are given in the section **Examples,** for no instructions are given with the exercises themselves. Most are self-explanatory anyway.

Communication is a necessity of life and the better you are at it, the easier it is to succeed. The more words you have at your command the more persuasively you can present yourself. Effective communication is not about how many words you use, but about which words you select to use. You can only select the best words for the best occasions if you have a large vocabulary to draw from.

Not being able to express oneself is one of the most frustrating situations, as anyone who has heard the sound of a screaming baby knows. Self-confidence goes hand in hand with verbal ability – inarticulate people tend to be diffident because they cannot express themselves easily. The more words you have available to clarify and control how you speak and write, the more you can be in control of your life and relations with other people.

Many people find that they can recognize far more words than they can actively use. All too often a person's range of words is limited because a large part of his vocabulary remains passive, and not fully understood or utilized. It is only when you can explain what words mean that you can start to use them. A number of the exercises here, like **Define the difference** and **Test your understanding,** are intended to jog your passive knowledge of the language into active use.

Jargon and redundant words are the enemies of an effective and precise use of words. The section on **How not to improve your wordpower** gives practice in eliminating the redundancies in vocabulary. There are also exercises on rewriting clichés and changing nouns, adjectives, etc. into verbs. The trend in usage now is to use adverbs, nouns or adjectives in preference to verbs, often to the detriment of clear, direct expression. The section on **Foreign words and phrases** contains many of the foreign terms you are likely to find that have been absorbed into the English language.

It would be misleading to suggest that a good vocabulary does not necessitate a good grasp of grammar. Good speakers do not speak ungrammatically. However it is not within the scope of this book to set out the essential points of English grammar, although some common grammatical mistakes are to be found in the exercises on **Confusable words**.

One sure way of enriching your vocabulary is to be well read in the classics of English literature. Unfortunately, few people now have the time or inclination to read widely; television and magazines seem much less effort. Thus fewer and fewer people really appreciate how great our literary heritage is and how much there is to enjoy and learn from how our great writers use words.

Of course there are other, though less formative, ways of improving your wordpower than enjoying literature. An important habit to instil, which is not at all time-consuming, is to look up in the dictionary those words which you do not understand. It's surprising how many people do not bother to do this, preferring to make an inspired guess. By not making this small effort your passive vocabulary will grow, as will its inaccuracies, while your active vocabulary will stay the same size.

Finally, regard words as ends in themselves, not merely as means to an end. Some of the exercises here, like **Thinking about words** and

Couplets, are more a test of your inventiveness and creativity, rather than the range of your vocabulary. Learning new words should be enjoyable, as well as useful. A love of language embraces innumerable other issues, such as literature, history and psychology; if you care about words you will certainly never be bored.

Examples

EXERCISES TESTING RANGE OF VOCABULARY AND GENERAL VERBAL SKILLS

1. Synonyms (or words with similar meanings).
You must find the correct synonym for the word given. The first and last letters of the answer are shown, for example:

sex   g . . . . r

(Answer: gender)

2. Find the rhyme.
For each quesiton you must find the right word which rhymes with the second word of the pair and is similar in meaning to the first, for example:

valley, tail = v . . e

(Answer: vale)

3. Words with more than one meaning.
You must insert the word that means the same as the words outside the brackets, for example:

reduction (. . .) incision

(Answer: cut)

4. Single words.
Each sentence in the exercise has a phrase in *italics* which must be replaced by one word which does not change the meaning, for example:

Half the patients were given the real drug, and half the *dummy pill.*

(Answer: placebo)

5. Antonyms (or words with opposite meanings).
You must find the correct antonym for the word given. The first and last letters of the answer are shown, for example:

loyal   t . . . . s

(Answer: traitorous)

6. The odd man out.
You must find the odd man out in each group of words, for example:

ruin, wreck, instruct, spoil, disable

(Answer: instruct)

EXERCISES TESTING VISUAL ABILITY WITH WORDS

1. Find the hidden word
Each sentence conceals a word, if you combine some of the last letters of one of the words with the first letters of the following word. Sometimes all the letters of one word may be involved, and sometimes the hidden word may bridge three in the sentence. Often more than one may be hidden. For example:

He came looking for me after ringing.

(Answer: camel, form/forme, err/erring)

2. Mischmasch.

This game was invented by Lewis Carroll, who devised many word games. A group of letters is given, and you must find a word that contains the letters in the order given. There may be several words possible for each group, for example:

ppr

(Answer: oppression, apprehend, suppress, etc. In the answer section we have given one example only.)

3. Anagrams.

A true anagram is a word formed by the letters of another in different order. In this game, however, the other word is a nonsensical jumble; you must first unravel them all, then find the odd one out, for example:

HTAMSCO
LEDUHOSR
OFOR
BEWOL

(Answer: stomach, shoulder, roof, elbow – so the odd one out is roof, all the others being parts of the body.)

4. Find the word ending.

You must find out which group of letters can be preceded by all the letters given, so that proper words are formed. For example:

L
R
CH
H   ...
N
P
TH

(Answer: OSE – which makes lose, rose, chose, hose, nose, pose, those.)

5. The linking word.
In each question you must insert the word that completes the first word and begins the second, for example:

voy(...)nda

(Answer: age = voyage/agenda)

EXERCISES TESTING CREATIVE ABILITY

1. Thinking about words.
An exercise to test how aware you are of the qualities associated with words. There are no 'correct' answers to these questions. For example:

What's the silliest word you can think of?

(Suggested answer: blub)

2. Couplets
You may be given two words with which you must make a rhyming couplet, or you may have to make up the second line. It doesn't matter how nonsensical the couplet is (within reason), but remember to keep the lines roughly similar in length. For example:

seal; feel

(Possible answer: The penguin and the seal
                Freezing water do not feel)

3. Find the words.
You must make as many words as you can from the letters of a given word, for example:

ground

(Answer: run, gun, rug, round, dour, rung, dung, dug, god, rod,

our, gourd, nod, nor, dog, dun, don, drug, undo, duo, etc. Two-letter
words are possible, of course, but we have omitted these from the
answer section, and limited the selection to ten words for each
question.)

4. Making words.
You are given two letters and must find at least ten words which begin
with these letters. Do not use derivatives; you may not write *friendship*
as well as *friend*, if the two letters are *fr*. More importantly, don't use
a dictionary! For example:

sp

(Answer: special, speck, spatial, sponge, spurious, spark, spooky,
speed, spray, spring, etc.)

EXERCISES TESTING PRECISION IN USING WORDS

1. What's the difference?
You are given two words and you have to define the difference between
them. For example:

grief; sadness

(Suggested answer: Grief is a much deeper sorrow than sadness. If
a friend dies, one feels grief; if a friend goes away for a long time,
one feels sadness.

2. Test your understanding.
You are given two words with which you must make up a sentence,
showing that you know what they mean. For example:

pertinent; remarks

(Possible answer: During the discussion he made some pertinent
remarks which everyone appreciated.)

3. The nearest definition.

You are given one word with four possible definitions of it (some of these may be quite wrong). You have to select whichever you think is correct or closest. For example, is 'charisma'

(a) a charming personality?
(b) charm?
(c) the ability to inspire followers with devotion and enthusiasm?
(d) a special aura that some people have, which draws others to them?

(Answer: (c))

4. Confusable words.

You are given a sentence which you have to complete with the correct word, for example:

I have not read the ... of the book. (*foreward, foreword*)

(Answer: foreword)

WORD GAME

Doublets. This is another game invented by Lewis Carroll. Two words of the same length are given and you have to transform the first into the last by progressing through a series of words in which each differs from the next by one letter only. The object is to make the series as short as possible. You may rearrange the letters of a word instead of introducing a new letter, but you may not do both. In this game you are permitted to use a dictionary – it may well help you when stuck! For example:

Change *none* into *some*

(Answer: none
      tone
      tome
      some)

The Exercises

Exercise 1 – Find the rhyme

1. Snoop, fly = S.y
2. Trauma, rock = S...k
3. Transparent, fear = C...r
4. Spacious, gloomy = R...y
5. Fight, cattle = B....e
6. Parry, alert = A...t
7. Restrain, herb = C..b
8. Tithe, heavy = L..y
9. Overflow, seam = T..m
10. Achievement, heat = F..t

Exercise 2 – Find the hidden word

1. I am learning the art of public speaking.
2. The mad dentist was arrested.
3. Who ever heard of a fat heroine?
4. This is a plea for the defence.
5. Sarah's car lets her be independent.
6. Algebra induces headaches.
7. The spectacle very much reminds me of Rome.
8. Do not trip lest you injure yourself.
9. The mysterious nomad ventures his opinion.
10. Do not show antipathy, please.

Exercise 3 – Synonyms

1. Shy   T...d
2. Enjoyment   P.....e
3. Pattern   S...e
4. Change   A...r

5.	Mystery	R . . . . e
6.	Angry	F . . . . s
7.	Seldom	R . . . . y
8.	Dawn	S . . . . . e
9.	Brave	C . . . . s
10.	Parcel	P . . . . . e

Exercise 4 – Single words

1. It will be a *help and a benefit* to you to know the number of competitors.
2. Although he had many friends he lacked *close familiarity* with any of them.
3. The water is only *slightly hot*.
4. She was continually *changing her view* between the first choice and the second.
5. This man is guilty of *murdering his father*.
6. He had no *pricks of conscience* about borrowing money from his grandmother.
7. As a child she was *excessively fearful* of strange dogs.
8. Drink *sensibly and sparingly* and you will stay healthy.
9. *Put back* your head on the headrest.
10. His bathroom was *dirty and squalid*.

Exercise 5 – Mischmasch

1. lho
2. cti
3. mpe
4. utr
5. iff
6. tym
7. rdl
8. ypn
9. ilo
10. ula

18

Exercise 6 – What's the difference?

1. Capable; efficient
2. Energetic; athletic
3. Deceptive; deceitful
4. Irritate; exasperate
5. Labour; work
6. Teach; instruct
7. Comply; agree
8. Lazy; languid
9. Poignant; moving
10. Cold; frigid

Exercise 7 – The linking word

1. o(. . .)ace
2. wind(. . . .)acy
3. s(. . . .)ful
4. vaga(. . . .)age
5. bo(. . . . .)age
6. p(. . .)uage
7. re(. . . . .)tain
8. con(. . . .)ature
9. ho(. . .)less
10. ori(. . .)gham

Exercise 8 – Thinking about words

1. What's the funniest word you can think of?
2. What's the most boring word you can think of?
3. What's the most pompous word or phrase you can think of?
4. What's the most poetic word or phrase you can think of?
5. What's the most difficult word to say that you can think of?

Exercise 9 – Doublets

1. Change *find* into *lose.*
2. Change *mother* into *father.*
3. Change *dry* into *wet.*
4. Change *sea* into *sky.*
5. Change *ill* into *fit.*

Exercise 10 – Test your understanding

1. extinction; protected species
2. surveillance; suspect
3. obsequious; crawl
4. sophistry; persuade
5. clandestine; conspiracy
5. nostrum; cure
7. recondite; subject
8. faction; support
9. consent; marriage
10. proselyte; convert

Exercise 11 – Confusable words

1. This will have a dramatic . . . on him. *(affect, effect)*
2. She was not . . . of his hard work. *(appreciative, appreciable)*
3. The bag was made of . . . . *(canvass, canvas)*
4. The children are no longer . . . on their father. *(dependent, dependant)*
5. He was . . . in her enthusiastic reminiscences. *(disinterested, uninterested)*
6. At school she would . . . every rule. *(flout, flaunt)*
7. With the deadline approaching, the pressure was . . . . *(intensive, intense)*
8. The virtuoso's performance was . . . . *(masterly, masterful)*
9. We walked down a . . . slope. *(precipitate, precipitous)*
10. The price of fruit varies according to . . . changes *(seasonal, seasonable)*

Exercise 12 – Anagrams

1. TASKE
   CLICULHRH
   RBOYN
   HRAECCU

2. IYLL
   OKA
   CEBHE
   EMLI

3. TULFE
   EBOO
   ILOVIN
   RLACIETN

4. AVN
   USB
   NIRAT
   RYROL

5. SPIAR
   DMDIAR
   MREO
   NPISA

6. TNIDSET
   UJEGD
   TRBIERSAR
   IOLOTSCIR

7. HRACI
   EHUSO
   BALET
   OTOSL

8. NTNESI
   TDYUS
   LOPO
   GYRBU

9. SVTE
   SRUTORES
   ALWTEL
   SBULOE

10. SPETIR
    RCORGE
    ATIOLR
    KARBE

Exercise 13 – The odd man out *y*

1. helpless, impotent, defenceless, protected, prostrated
2. violin, piano, cello, mandolin, viola
3. smell, aroma, flavour, fragrance, scent
4. worsen, decline, deteriorate, decay, damage
5. church, mosque, chapel, cathedral, abbey
6. strong, energetic, robust, attractive, fit
7. oak, poplar, beech, fern, cedar
8. interesting, important, significant, notable, material
9. insert, inundate, implant, instil, impregnate
10. flood, soak, splash, pour, shower

Exercise 14 – Find the words

1. Instrumental   2. Anniversary   3. Establishment   4. Biography
5. Cauliflower   6. Providence   7. Outshine   8. Throughout
9. Consume   10. Countenance

Exercise 15 – Couplets

1. tune; spoon
2. spree; tree
3. coax; hoax
4. lame; game
5. rambler; gambler

Exercise 16 – Antonyms

1.	Eloquent	I . . . . e
2.	Lively	L . . . . . . s
3.	Extrovert	I . . . . t
4.	Haphazard	O . . . . d
5.	Religious	I . . . . s
6.	Tender	U . . . . g
7.	Disinterested	P l
8.	Hopeful	H . . . . . . s
9.	Opportune	I . . . . e
10.	Definite	U . . . . n

Exercise 17 – Find the word ending

1.	B		4.	N	
	K			R	
	D			T	
	G	...		P	...
	M			Z	
	P			W	
	WH			B	
2.	L		5.	M	
	T			T	
	BR			ST	
	S	...		F	...
	FL			B	
	M			W	
	N			GU	
3.	D		6.	G	
	R			M	
	S			R	
	H	...		P	...
	F			L	
	N			D	
	W			GR	

7.	STR		9.	D	
	R			T	
	W			L	
	SN	...		SL	...
	P			CH	
	GR			M	
	TR			GR	
8.	J		10.	TR	
	GL			AB	
	M			SH	
	F	...		FL	...
	W			P	
	TR			B	
	B			R	

Exercise 18 – Words with more than one meaning

1. healthy (. . . .) spring
2. list (. . . .) bap
3. boulder (. . . .) sway
4. ruin (. . . . .) damage
5. attractiveness (. . . . .) spell
6. contemporary (. . . . . . .) course
7. come near (. . . . .) surroundings
8. price (. . . . . .) entrust
9. soldier (. . . . . . .) confidential
10. weep (. . .) exclaim

Exercise 19 – Find the rhyme

1. Lie, surgery = P . . . . . y
2. Lament, scourge = D . . . e
3. Appearance, size = G . . . e
4. Resource, ingredient = E . . . . t
5. Manner, mile = S . . . e
6. Infectious, outrageous = C . . . . s

7. Diminish, seduce = R . . . . e
8. Traumatic, narrowing = H . . . . g
9. Weary, faded = J . . . d
10. Fancy, hymn = W . . m

Exercise 20 – Find the hidden word

1. The strange demi-god descended from above.
2. He could hum and whistle simultaneously.
3. This function always plays up.
4. Come lyre, play on.
5. The ground about the house was full of rocks.
6. I do not know whether to edit or rewrite this.
7. She wants all owls to be protected.
8. Don't whisper, juryman, speak up.
9. Go back to the rear, then turn left.
10. The man at the helm, eternally vigilant.

Exercise 21 – Synonyms

1. Pillar   C . . . . n
2. Force   S . . . . . h
3. Surprising   U . . . . d
4. Goal   T . . . . t
5. Honest   F . . . k
6. Branch   B . . . h
7. Tepid   L . . . . . . m
8. Found   E . . . . . . h
9. Premature   E . . . y
10. Final   U . . . . . e

Exercise 22 – Single words

1. The *ancient and unspoiled* manuscript is at the auction house.
2. That is a *stain on his character* that he does not deserve.

3. Being *generous and noble* she overlooked his outburst.
4. His *dislike of mankind* makes him reclusive.
5. The Royal Family are forever being *hounded and harrassed* by the media.
6. The officials dined on the *raised platform* at the end of the hall.
7. Most people have the *right to vote* at elections.
8. I need a *stimulus and incentive* to carry on writing.
9. Her expression was *shining and joyous*.
10. The general *spread out* the troops around the enemy camp.

Exercise 23 – Mischmasch

1. cuu   2. ssi   3. agr   4. gne   5. coc
6. eze   7. dox   8. psh   9. rbl   10. ius

Exercise 24 – What's the difference?

1. Undo; untie
2. Primitive; barbaric
3. Succeed; achieve
4. Bypass; avoid
5. Defend; protect
6. Sufficient; ample
7. Painful; excruciating
8. Friend; comrade
9. Superior; supercilious
10. Ambiguous; equivocal

Exercise 25 – The linking word

1. c(. . .)ter
2. eye(. . . .)se
3. up(. . . . .)eous
4. m(. . . . .)ance
5. fl(. . .)rage
6. re(. . . . . . .)ion

7. hat(. . .)olent
8. at(. . . .)er
9. pro(. . . .)ament
10. bar(. . . .)say

Exercise 26 – Thinking about words

1. What's the most sinister word or phrase that you can think of?
2. What's the most meaningless word or phrase that you can think of?
3. What's the most childish word that you can think of?
4. What's the most mechanical word that you can think of?
5. What's the most domestic word that you can think of?

Exercise 27 – Doublets

1. Change *hard* into *soft*.
2. Change *white* into *black*.
3. Change *evil* into *good*.
4. Change *tree* into *wood*.
5. Change *tell* into *time*.

Exercise 28 – Test your understanding

1. gambol; lambs
2. mordant; unattractive
3. solve; intractable
4. menagerie; animals
5. contrition; guilt
6. hierarchy; firm
7. raillery; blunder
8. hypnosis; addictions
9. gratuity; reward
10. soliloquize, hero

Exercise 29 – Confusable words

1. The difference was .... .*(negligent, negligible)*
2. It was a very ... hotel. *(luxurious, luxuriant)*
3. He was ... about how the dinner table looked. *(punctual; punctilious)*
4. He got to the point in a painfully ... way. *(torturous, tortuous)*
5. The chairman looked embarrassed at the ... speech. *(turgid, turbid)*
6. There is one last ... if all else fails. *(resource, resort)*
7. If the solution is ..., we can start now. *(practicable, practical)*
8. It was a ... reply. *(judicial, judicious)*
9. The ... of the problem is dreadful. *(enormity, magnitude)*
10. I ... that you don't wish to come. *(imply, infer)*

Exercise 30 – Anagrams

1. CTODRO
    CTAHERE
    RWLYEA
    TEDSUTN

2. LBWUGNAO
    TAREPATMN
    RDUNGAE
    NINSOMA

3. NTEWRI
    PNISGR
    SREEAT
    ATMUNU

4. LUFRO
    LBEYRA
    AHWTE
    ATOS

5. BURY
    PIHSRPAE
    RLDEMEA
    RVISLE

6. NSOW
    AHIL
    NDIW
    ELETS

7. KLAEN
    HICN
    ECEKHS
    ERBWOEY

8. SUEDL
    ETBELE
    ERGFAIF
    EPECITNED

9. EFCRHN
    DNIAI
    IATNLIA
    AENBLGI

10. VEBOENTEH
    ENDCIKS
    CBAH
    HBMARS

Exercise 31 – The odd man out

1. amusing, entertaining, embarrassing, funny, comic
2. exacting, expensive, extortionate, costly, exorbitant
3. city, country, town, capital, metropolis
4. pyrotechnics, display, flourish, parade, crowd

5. report, inform, converse, tell, communicate
6. acquire, gain, procure, possess, obtain
7. coast, sail, drive, navigate, row
8. agreement, reconciliation, accord, concord, alliance
9. invent, imagine, conceive, devise, begin
10. extraneous, exiguous, scanty, meagre, small

Exercise 32 – Find the words

1. Apparition
2. Withdrawal
3. Argument
4. Gratitude
5. Reputation
6. Extraordinary
7. Propagate
8. Whisper
9. Adventure
10. Language

Exercise 33 – Couplets

1. herd; word
2. hurled; world
3. laid; paid
4. chatter; matter
5. blithe; scythe

Exercise 34 – Antonyms

1. Enthusiasm   A....y
2. Wayward   O......t
3. Slim   O...e
4. Puny   S....g
5. Justice   I.......e
6. Sly   C....d
7. Rash   P.....t
8. Improve   D........e
9. Leader   F......r
10. Ordinary   E..........y

Exercise 35 – Find the word ending

1. DR
   B
   S
   T   ...
   STR
   GL
   R

2. GR
   BR
   HAR
   M   ...
   B
   P
   GL

3. L
   ST
   CR
   D   ...
   R
   C
   TR

4. C
   B
   V
   W   ...
   P
   L
   S

5. ST
   B
   C
   DR   ...
   T
   N
   PR

6. C
   F
   ST
   P   ...
   SP
   DR

7. TR
   J
   P
   B   ...
   L
   SL
   D

8. M
   TR
   B
   S   ...
   WH
   N
   GR

9. T
   ST
   FL
   M   ...
   P
   D
   L

10. T
    L
    S
    G   ...
    N
    FR
    C

Exercise 36 – Words with more than one meaning

1. begin (. . . . .) jump
2. regulation (. . . .) govern
3. form (. . . . .) mould
4. foundation (. . . .) despicable
5. heath (. . . . .) clear
6. progress (. . . . . . .) fee
7. refinement (. . . . .) thanksgiving
8. fib (. . .) recline
9. ticket (. . . .) food
10. darkness (. . . . .) despondency

Exercise 37 – Find the hidden word

1. The garden seat is comfortable.
2. His laugh terrified her.
3. In the field, rape, rye-grass and poppies were growing.
4. Go, settle yourself and relax.
5. The icon fronts upon the altar.
6. Oh apple peel ingeniously sculptured!
7. It will occur ninety times.
8. There, members, take heed.
9. The foxes chewed the meat thoughtfully.
10. When you doze, never snore.

Exercise 38 – Synonyms

1. Peevish   I . . . . . . e
2. Entrance   C . . . m
3. Interview   M . . . . . g
4. Model   P . . . . n
5. Confuse   B . . . . . r
6. Reduction   D . . . . . e
7. Mutual   S . . . . d
8. Heave   H . . . t
9. Changeable   F . . . . e
10. Ebullient   E . . . . t

Exercise 39 – Single words

1. I hated his *cloying and excessive* flattery.
2. This is supposed to be a *cure for all ills.*
3. His article was not balanced, but *intended to promote a particular viewpoint.*
4. The *manager of the theatre company* was a lively guest.
5. It was a *mutually destructive* war.
6. The *tree garden* in the park is famous.
7. He was a *man who had once again fallen into crime.*
8. When I'm fifty, I'm going to write the *story of my life.*
9. It is a *composition for a full orchestra with three or four movements.*
10. I can't bear his *fondness for pompous moralizing.*

Exercise 40 – Mischmasch

1.	bsu	6.	hro
2.	tto	7.	bdu
3.	bbo	8.	ogr
4.	oga	9.	rdi
5.	alp	10.	gge

Exercise 41 – What's the difference?

1. Trivial; frivolous
2. Aggressive; violent
3. Rancour; bitterness
4. Plan; policy
5. Germane; relevant
6. Optimistic; bullish
7. Chronology; history
8. Review; inquiry
9. Vocation; occupation
10. Innocent; ingenuous

Exercise 42 – The linking word

1. d(. . . .)y
2. s(. . . .)rait
3. f(. . .)gano
4. con(. . . .)ile
5. re(. . . .)ion
6. s(. . . . .)ening
7. hap(. . .)dulum
8. mar(. . . .)ow
9. sug(. . . .)ure
10. a(. . . .)ful

Exercise 43 – Thinking about words

1. What's your grandmother's favourite phrase?
2. Suggest a phrase or word that politicians love to use.
3. What's your favourite onomatopoeic word?
4. What's the most exotic word that you can think of?
5. What's the most delicate word that you can think of?

Exercise 44 – Doublets

1. Change *head* into *foot*.
2. Change *work* into *rest*.
3. Change *tame* into *wild*.
4. Change *love* into *hate*.
5. Change *rise* into *fall*.

Exercise 45 – Test your understanding

1. scotch; impossible
2. headmistress; homily
3. conversation; desultory
4. draconian; restrictions
5. apocryphal; story

6. marsupial; kangaroo
7. sinecure; job
8. pseudonym; write
9. precursor; company
10. gratuitous; remarks

Exercise 46 – Confusable words

1. The . . . kitchen was gleaming and immaculate. *(new, pristine)*.
2. He had always been . . ., anxious to please. *(complacent, complaisant)*
3. The discussion was prolonged by . . . interruptions. *(continuous, continual)*
4. He was a . . . academic. *(distinctive, distinguished)*
5. We must prepare ourselves for the . . . crisis. *(imminent, eminent)*
6. Because of over-crowding greater restrictions are being brought against . . . *(emigrants, immigrants)*
7. Everyone despised their . . . behaviour. *(contemptuous, contemptible)*
8. As an . . . route, you can go through Winchester. *(alternate, alternative)*
9. He was a . . . man, whom we all loved. *(benevolent, beneficient)*
10. That was a . . . film. *(titivating, titillating)*

Exercise 47 – Anagrams

1. RQSUAE
   EGLINTRA
   CLCEIR
   ASCSOMP

2. MEBLCUR
   ATRT
   HCEKCNI
   BSROTE

3. TIPAN
   ENGER
   WLOYLE
   CLBKA

4. ALASTUARI
   EEGECR
   LODLHAN
   MEGYANR

5. AHECAEDH
   TRENEPS
   FZELIUNAN
   EFRVE

6. FHTET
   EMRUDR
   TAHDE
   DURAF

7. CRETNOC
   IMLF
   PYAL
   DUTSOI

8. RERIV
   HRUCHC
   KELA
   RMASET

9. RPCEPO
   OTCTNO
   OYCRUDODR
   ISLK

10. CGMEIRA
    LMSEI
    COHTU
    NFORW

Exercise 48 – The odd man out

1. correct, proper, right, absolute, true
2. law, constitution, instruction, statute, act
3. devout, sanctimonious, pious, religious, reverent
4. cure, care, heal, mend, restore
5. trick, cheat, deceive, injure, delude
6. sleepy, lazy, idle, indolent, slothful
7. prophet, augur, medium, soothsayer, seer
8. exonerate, exculpate, acquit, clear, forgive
9. quibble, equivocate, cavil, argue, subtilize
10. adjournment, revision, suspension, moratorium, postponement

Exercise 49 – Find the words

1. Interior
2. Disastrous
3. Progressive
4. Fatigue
5. Enthusiasm
6. Technique
7. Apprentice
8. Characteristic
9. Reproach
10. Professional

Exercise 50 – Couplets

1. She was amazed when he revealed/. . .
2. Never say it is too late/. . .
3. The French are said to be stiff and proud/. . .
4. My father to my mother said/. . .
5. The suntan is a modern craze/. . .

Exercise 51 – Antonyms

1. Monarchy   R c
2. Selfish   P c
3. Balanced   U . . . . . .e
4. Anxious   S . . . .e
5. Emphatic   U . . . . .d
6. Junior   S . . . .r
7. Soaked   P . . . .d

8.	Excessive	I . . . . t
9.	Forthcoming	R . . . . . . t
10.	Imprudent	C . . . . t

Exercise 52 – Find the word ending

1. GA
    SH
    R
    H   ...
    BL
    TA
    FLA

2. ST
    C
    D
    W   ...
    M
    B
    R

3. G
    CR
    FR
    DR   ...
    D
    S
    M

4. S
    CR
    SL
    D   ...
    J
    ST
    SH

5. R
    TH
    BR
    S   ...
    W
    WR
    SL

6. S
    ST
    R
    W   ...
    P
    C
    IM

7. B
    CR
    M
    N   ...
    S
    SW
    SP

8. F
    CL
    R
    B   ...
    D
    W
    H

9.		10.	
	M		BL
	S		T
	C		S
	B ...		H ...
	L		KN
	R		B
	SH		R

Exercise 53 – Words with more than one meaning

1. finish (. . .) purpose
2. impoverished (. . . .) unfortunate
3. just (. . . .) blond
4. faithful (. . . .) right
5. stop work (. . . . . .) hit
6. competition (. . . . . . .) contend
7. wallet (. . . . .) wrinkle
8. succeed (. . . .) proceed
9. squeeze (. . . . .) printing-house
10. tendency (. . . . .) religious dress

Exercise 54 – The nearest definition

1. QUIBBLE: (a) eat fussily. (b) tell untruth. (c) play on words. (d) be ambiguous.
2. OPINE: (a) hold opinion. (b) miss somebody. (c) think. (d) believe.
3. NICE: (a) pleasant. (b) particular. (c) lovely. (d) fine.
4. ANTIQUATED: (a) of antique value. (b) particular. (c) lovely. (d) fine.
5. CAUSTIC: (a) with cause. (b) burning, corroding substance. (c) sarcastic. (d) giving cause to.
6. MARATHON: (a) sweet. (b) race. (c) feat of endurance. (d) competition.
7. MORIBUND: (a) dead. (b) dying. (c) at point of death. (d) type of grave.

8. PLATITUDE: (a) commonplace. (b) saying. (c) proverb. (d) riddle.
9. DISMEMBER: (a) wrench. (b) member in disgrace. (c) tear limbs from. (d) dissect.
10. ATAVISTIC: (a) resembling parents. (b) old-fashioned. (c) historic. (d) resembling ancestors.

Exercise 55 – Find the rhyme

1. Candle, caper = T...r
2. Plan, revise = D....e
3. Struggle, apple = G.....e
4. Clash, bar = J.r
5. Horizontal, opine = S....e
6. Weaken, capitulate = D.......e
7. Noose, falter = H....r
8. Finish, defeat = C......e
9. Solemn, brave = G...e
10. Decorative, sedate = O....e

Exercise 56 – Making words

1. Fr
2. Ab
3. Po
4. Sp
5. Mi
6. We
7. My
8. Do
9. Ru
10. Sk

Exercise 57 – Find the hidden word

1. I found him patiently waiting.
2. Her wit, her originality and her beauty amaze me.
3. Please pass, aged man.
4. The sea sonorously shook the sand.
5. From afar church bells were ringing.
6. She likes cream cheese too much.
7. It was a lush, old and quiet garden.
8. The marble bust leans perilously.

9. The importunate car petitioned unwary pedestrians.
10. There, sign your name please.

Exercise 58 – Synonyms

1. Right   E. . .t
2. Sly   C. . . . . .g
3. Agreeable   C. l
4. Perilous   P. . . . . . .s
5. Irresolute   H. . . . . .t
6. Screen   V. .l
7. Banish   O. . . . . .e
8. Defer   S. . . .t
9. Terrify   P. . . . .y
10. Bestow   B. . . . .h

Exercise 59 – Mischmasch

1. jej   6. uit
2. cca   7. dge
3. xtr   8. ior
4. dav   9. ill
5. ndo   10. ata

Exercise 60 – What's the difference?

1. Reign; rule
2. Alternative (n.); option
3. Fastidious; particular
4. Promise; swear
5. Bright; radiant
6. Capricious; volatile
7. Solicitous; concerned
8. Siesta; rest
9. Rough; coarse
10. Annual; perennial

Exercise 61 – Single words

1. The garden has been *magically transformed!*
2. The statue is *of indeterminate sex.*
3. She is doing her *apprenticeship as a trainee journalist.*
4. The judge heard the *various charges.*
5. The disease is *continually breaking out* in this impoverished country.
6. The Mutiny of 1857 was sparked off by a revolt amongst the *Indian soldiers.*
7. This issue is *about the meaning of words.*
8. The *pointed hood* almost concealed the monk's face.
9. My grandfather is now *forgetful and helpless.*
10. You will find your letters at the *General Post Office which keeps foreign letters.*

Exercise 62 – The linking word

1. ear(. . . .)le
2. l(. . . . .)ways
3. t(. . .)rture
4. ma(. . . .)ship
5. rail(. . .)side
6. ap(. . . .)l
7. d(. . .)er
8. b(. . . .)adaisical
9. s(. . .)riage
10. s(. . .)az

Exercise 63 – Couplets

1. caught; fought
2. stole; hole
3. stitch; hitch
4. fame, maim
5. botched; scotched

Exercise 64 – Doublets

1. Change *give* into *take.*
2. Change *dawn* into *dusk.*
3. Change *wine* into *tail.*
4. Change *cat* into *dog.*
5. Change *shame* into *blame.*

Exercise 65 – Test your understanding

1. camellias; spring
2. heckle; interrupt
3. scandal; tarnish
4. sonata; piano
5. cathedral; gargoyle
6. meritricious; praise
7. cognoscenti; book
8. calling; priest
9. bracing; December
10. Act; opera

Exercise 66 – Confusable words

1. It is the . . . that matters. *(principle, principal)*
2. He introduced the speaker very . . . . *(formerly, formally)*
3. It is an . . . plan. *(ingenuous, ingenious)*
4. The sad . . . of victims was read out. *(litany, list)*
5. She was very sociable, with a vast . . . of friends. *(array, panoply)*
6. Endless . . . stretched ahead. *(planes, plains)*
7. The fire . . . the wood to the ground. *(razed, raised)*
8. The . . . fired two shots. *(cannon, canon)*
9. I shall . . . that question. *(wave, waive)*
10. The car was . . . at the time. *(stationery, stationary)*

Exercise 67 – Anagrams

1. VLONE
   EPMO
   MFLI
   SYSAE

2. BRBRUE
   KIBRC
   MTEECN
   BALMER

3. RLIA
   EQEHCU
   LSLAODR
   GSITLENR

4. UGLAH
   KCHEUCL
   LGGEIG
   THOSU

5. WLEOB
   IISR
   LPIPU
   TARNEI

6. CENEI
   NCUISO
   NRIFED
   PWEENH

7. ODOLEP
   SOHER
   TALNAISA
   ISNAPEL

8. SBEKTA
   OTCA
   CLESTAH
   SACITSUE

9. NTIMEU
    RUOH
    AYER
    CNEDSO

10. NHABCR
    DRAO
    KRNUT
    GWTI

Exercise 68 – Find the words

1. Democracy
2. Pastoral
3. Mahogany
4. Reservoir
5. Vegetable
6. Cultural
7. Nostalgia
8. Fellow
9. Concentrate
10. Engrave

Exercise 69 – The odd man out

1. different, divergent, distinguished, discrepant, contrasting
2. model, paradigm, imitation, exemplar, representation.
3. humour, banter, raillery, persiflage, ridicule
4. desert, retreat, depart, flee, move
5. imperious, pedantic, dictatorial, peremptory, dogmatic
6. refuse, deny, gainsay, keep, withold
7. nave, aisle, altar, choir, steeple
8. dissent, acknowledge, disagreement, schism, protest
9. volcanic, chalk, lime, clay, sea
10. triple, double, couple, duplicate, twin

Exercise 70 – Making words

1. Er
2. Ke
3. Bu
4. Fl
5. Os
6. Ra
7. In
8. Ve
9. Gr
10. Em

Exercise 71 – Antonyms

1. Fertile   B. . . .n
2. Carnivore   H. . . . . . .e
3. Treeless   B. . .y
4. Hero   V. . . . .n
5. Imprison   L. . . . . .e
6. Normal   A. l
7. Resident   V. . . . .r
8. Zenith   N. . .r
9. Serious   I. . . . . . . .t
10. Frequent   I. . . . . . . .t

Exercise 72 – Find the word ending

1. S
   R
   M
   K   ...
   B
   WH
   TR

2. M
   D
   SH
   S   ...
   F
   W
   T

3. SH
   GL
   B
   C   ...
   SL
   P
   L

4. L
   O
   P
   BO   ...
   V
   M
   C

5. L
   B
   S
   GR   ...
   W
   ST
   H

6. S
   TH
   WR
   PR   ...
   L
   G
   THR

7.	T	9.	H
	GR		R
	C		TR
	DR ...		GR ...
	G		C
	N		M
	SH		L

8.	B	10.	ST
	S		THR
	J		B
	ST ...		GL ...
	D		M
	P		C
	L		G

Exercise 73 – The nearest definition

1. SHROUD: (a) sheet. (b) garment for the dead. (c) shoe for the dead. (d) type of material.
2. VISION: (a) dream. (b) sight. (c) view. (d) nightmare.
3. FAITH: (a) religious creed. (b) religious condition. (c) trust in or reliance on. (d) belief.
4. COMPLEMENT: (a) something which completes. (b) flattering remark. (c) completion. (d) pleasant remark.
5. CHICANERY: (a) trick. (b) legal trickery. (c) chicken dish. (d) legal saying.
6. ECCENTRIC: (a) mad. (b) bizarre. (c) odd. (d) demented.
7. MORALE: (a) moral question. (b) feelings. (c) morality. (d) moral condition.
8. MANDATORY: (a) necessary. (b) essential. (c) compulsory. (d) jaw-like.
9. PALIMPSEST: (a) artefact. (b) type of manuscript. (c) handwriting. (d) sea creature.
10. PRELUDE: (a) introductory performance, action etc. (b) first chapter of novel. (c) bishop. (d) introduction.

Exercise 74 – Words with more than one meaning

1. alter (. . . . . .) money
2. construct (. . . . .) border
3. applaud (. . . . .) encourage
4. stagger (. . . .) dance
5. abandon (. . . . . . .) wasteland
6. image (. . . . . . .) number
7. committee (. . . . . .) embark
8. correct (. . . . .) claim
9. agreement (. . . . .) shrink
10. result (. . . . .) children

Exercise 75 – Find the rhyme

1. Discriminating, elective = S. . . . . . .e
2. Collect, resemble = A. . . . . .e
3. Respond, exact = R. . .t
4. Container, spectacle = R. . . . . . . .e
5. Change, halter = A. . .r
6. Injure, fame = M. .m
7. Understand, clasp = G. . .p
8. Hide, gale = V. .l
9. Frantic, septic = H. . . .c
10. Legend, pith = M. .h

Exercies 76 – Find the hidden word

1. Is a greedy man better than a miser?
2. I am going to claim aid for this.
3. Always stir edible mushrooms when cooking.
4. The gullible mishear what people are really saying.
5. If you win, centuries of tradition will be broken.
6. The crab beyond the pool scuttled away.
7. The fad exhausted itself soon enough.
8. This serene German is delightful.
9. Those ten, dear children are playing together.
10. The grass had every blade cut to an equal length.

48

Exercise 77 – Synonyms

1.	Bombastic	T. . . .d
2.	Amusing	C. . .c
3.	Compete	R. . .l
4.	Try	S. . . .e
5.	Worsen	D. . . . .e
6.	Display	M. . . . . .t
7.	Contrivance	G. . . .t
8.	Strict	S. . . . . .t
9.	Propose	P. . . . .d
10.	Riddle	C. . . . . .m

Exercise 78 – Mischmasch

1.	sch	6.	ngu
2.	owa	7.	ssu
3.	cto	8.	rga
4.	xpl	9.	deg
5.	bst	10.	rmt

Exercise 79 – Single words

1. His way of living is *very disciplined, frugal and simple.*
2. The river *curves and winds* through the valley.
3. His regime was *tyrannical and oppressive.*
4. The conversation was *leaping from one subject to another.*
5. It is a *piece of land that projects far into the sea.*
6. I remain *unconvinced of the truth* of that explanation.
7. This is a *path for horses only.*
8. If he dies he will be seen as *someone who sacrificed himself to a cause.*
9. It is a typical *fifteenth century Italian* painting.
10. It is the *broad part of the river where it runs into the sea.*

Exercise 80 – What's the difference?

1. Embellish; decorate
2. Hide; lurk
3. Intelligent; clever
4. Sensual; sensuous
5. Cathartic; therapeutic
6. Wet; humid
7. Remote; distant
8. Chance; luck
9. Remove; depart
10. Question; query

Exercise 81 – Couplets

1. Today I'm lacking inspiration/. . .
2. Dear child, innocent of all harm/. . .
3. You we cordially invite/. . .
4. Venice, that fairytale on water/. . .
5. I really know no earthly reason/. . .

Exercise 82 – The linking word

1. fire(. . . .)er
2. p(. . .)man
3. b(. . . .)nt
4. g(. . . . .)about
5. at(. . . . .)ation
6. t(. . .)th
7. ad(. . . . .)ing
8. ball(. . . .)y
9. t(. . . .)l
10. s(. . . .)ative

Exercise 83 – Doublets

1. Change *word* into *deed*.
2. Change *book* into *film*.
3. Change *born* into *died*.
4. Change *loss* into *gain*.
5. Change *warm* into *cold*.

Exercise 84 – Test your understanding

1. bust; marble
2. parkland; ha-ha
3. fanatic; religion
4. saint; canonize
5. anathema; small talk
6. oils; paint
7. applicants; portfolio
8. intransigence; irritating
9. fallow; field
10. usher; seat

Exercise 85 – Confusable words

1. It was a ... meeting for which I was quite unprepared. *(fortuitous, fortunate)*
2. There are other people concerned ... you. *(beside, besides)*
3. This film has not been ...; it may not be suitable for children. *(censored, censured)*
4. Most tinned food is ... in vitamins. *(defective, deficient)*
5. The protest group ... the government official. *(deprecated, depreciated)*
6. The director gave an ... account of the year's turnover. *(exhausting, exhaustive)*
7. His contribution to the debate was .... . *(notable, notorious)*
8. Traditional ... are kept on this remembrance day. *(observations, observances)*

9. All his dealings with others are . . . and underhand. *(insidious, individious)*

10. It was a beautiful . . ., vast and wild. *(moor, more)*

Exercise 86 – Anagrams

1. MIA
   GTIFH
   DEN
   AGLO

2. DREONT
   EUSOM
   OSETITRO
   GRILEB

3. PAPEL
   RNPEU
   ALATSNU
   RCUNART

4. EHLE
   LESO
   HRCA
   KNCE

5. ALUTACELC
   DAD
   EDIR
   NUCOT

6. NWSIT
   YABB
   LUADQRPTUES
   TRTSPELI

7. NWULTA
   WFRELO
   GYAMAHON
   KEAT

8. VLONE
   LDUAIEGO
   TDBEEA
   LKTA

9. NHLUC
   PRUSPE
   LEPTA
   KAFSBARTE

10. KRTIC
    AYLP
    VEEDICE
    HACET

Exercise 87 – The odd man out

1. wife, mother, nephew, daughter, aunt
2. graveyard, cemetery, catacomb, church, mortuary
3. tennis, football, fishing, rugby, golf
4. communion, hymn, sermon, prayer, plea
5. neoclassical, gothic, perpendicular, rococo, floral
6. mound, valley, barrow, hillock, knoll
7. deprecate, criticize, speak, berate, chastise
8. moustache, beard, whiskers, nose, sideburns
9. shoe, hood, hat, cap, fez
10. flock, fish, shoal, brace, gaggle

Exercise 88 – Making words

1.	Go	6.	Le
2.	Ci	7.	Ro
3.	Kn	8.	Je
4.	Ta	9.	Qu
5.	Nu	10.	As

Exercise 89 – Antonyms

1.	Social	A........l
2.	Authentic	F..e
3.	Purposeful	A.....s
4.	Spontaneous	C........d
5.	Sane	D.....d
6.	Attractive	R.......t
7.	Formal	C....l
8.	Cultured	P........e
9.	Wise	F.....h
10.	Despair	H..e

Exercise 90 – Find the word ending

1. B
    SH
    C
    R   ...
    N
    T
    L

2. GR
    L
    D
    C   ...
    M
    GL
    PR

3. B
    D
    L
    SH   ...
    M
    P
    H

4. P
    L
    F
    M   ...
    D
    W
    BR

5. F
    SH
    C
    KN   ...
    T
    S
    B

6. GL
    GR
    B
    R   ...
    L
    D
    BR

7. C
    P
    W
    CH   ...
    H
    QU
    ST

9. R
    S
    TH
    W   ...
    ST
    K
    WR

8. B
    D
    L
    DR   ...
    BR
    ST
    KN

10. L
    F
    C
    D   ...
    P
    G
    H

Exercise 91 – Words with more than one meaning

1. mark (. . . . .) follow
2. celebration (. . . . .) group
3. accuse (. . . . . .) duty
4. desire (. . . .) lack
5. forehead (. . . .) hilltop
6. option (. . . . . .) select
7. said (. . . . .) part of wheel
8. reason (. . . . .) purpose
9. progressing (. . . . . .) affecting
10. hunt (. . . . . . .) hobby

Exercise 92 – The nearest definition

1. MOOT: (a) law court. (b) hearing. (c) law students' debate. (d) water bird.
2. TOURNAMENT: (a) game. (b) medieval competition for noblemen. (c) long tennis match. (d) sports contest.
3. JEROBOAM: (a) biblical character. (b) gigantic wine bottle. (c) large container. (d) vast urn.

4. BIRETTA: (a) small beret. (b) type of seed. (c) cap worn by Roman Catholic clergymen. (d) hat.
5. SANCTION: (a) holy blessing. (b) prohibition. (c) measure. (d) penalty for disobedience.
6. ABLUTION: (a) ceremonial washing. (b) careful personal hygiene. (c) cleansing. (d) cleaning.
7. CONSEQUENCE: (a) paper game. (b) result of preceding action. (c) conclusion. (d) outcome.
8. CHAMELEON: (a) cloth. (b) extinct reptile. (c) type of lizard. (d) inconstant.
9. PALPABLE: (a) soft. (b) tactile. (c) that can be touched or felt. (d) sensuous.
10. FANFARE: (a) short journey. (b) wave of fan. (c) piece of music for brass. (d) ceremonial sounding of trumpets.

Exercise 93 – Synonyms

1.	Tardy	D. . . . . .y
2.	Imagine	C. . . . . .e
3.	Demon	D. . . .n
4.	Accidental	F. . . . . . . .s
5.	Tend	M. . . . . .r
6.	Scowl	G. . . . .e
7.	Whiten	B. . . .h
8.	Entertaining	D. . . . . .g
9.	Amusing	D. . .l
10.	Head	P. .e

Exercise 94 – Find the rhyme

1. Stick, wane = C. .e
2. Visit, roar = T. .r
3. Frequent, gaunt = H. . .t
4. Fancy, flimsy = W. . . .y
5. Trivial, chivalrous = F. . . . . . .s
6. Plot, retire = C. . . . . .e
7. Establish, destitute = C. . . . . . . .e

8. Enticement, sepoy = D...y
9. Charm, miasma = C......a
10. Detective, truth = S....h

Exercise 95 – Find the hidden word

1. I don't care, sister.
2. The cab left early, but was still late.
3. I bet terrible things will happen.
4. He had vices, instead of virtues.
5. Come home always, my son.
6. Chloric exhaust fumes should be avoided.
7. Don't grab, lower yourself to ask.
8. A hideous mollusc rapped at my door.
9. He was fit, alert but inclined to be lazy.
10. The drab road cast a doubt in my mind.

Exercise 96 – Mischmasch

1.	mni	6.	mps
2.	lli	7.	cke
3.	wle	8.	asc
4.	alr	9.	rtu
5.	ntr	10.	ndu

Exercise 97 – Single words

1. I deny this *absolutely and completely.*
2. Our love of jargon is *emasculating and impoverishing* the language.
3. This is *the place where they unload the ships.*
4. It is *an area of land where young trees are grown.*
5. These foreign ships are being *denied entry into our ports.*
6. He is a religious man who is on a *journey to a sacred place as an act of devotion.*

7. I always enjoy the *glorious spectacle of* the carnival.
8. He has lost his *false teeth!*
9. We were forced to *sleep out without tents that night.*
10. At drama school she attends lessons to improve her *manner of speaking.*

Exercise 98 – What's the difference?

1. Collaborate; conspire
2. Cacophany; noise
3. Diction; speech
4. Define; explain
5. Derivation; origin
6. Realm; sphere
7. Rebuke; berate
8. Fashionable; stylish
9. Impressive; imposing
10. Terror; horror

Exercise 99 – The linking word

1. im(. . . . .)ure
2. dis(. . . . .)ful
3. c(. . . .)less
4. ex(. . . . .)ant
5. ar(. . . . .)r
6. b(. . .)er
7. re(. . . .)ways
8. mon(. . .)hole
9. at(. . . . .)or
10. sp(. . . .)let

Exercise 100 – Doublets

1. Change *game* into *test*.
2. Change *slow* into *fast*.
3. Change *flour* into *bread*.

4. Change *walk* into *trot*.
5. Change *solo* into *duet*.

Exercise 101 – Test your understanding

1. metals; crucible
2. acolytes; priest
3. Laodicean; opinions
4. rhadamanthine; headmaster
5. procrastinate; decision
6. curator; museum
7. dyslexic; spell
8. abstruse; explanation
9. factotum; manage
10. cortège; proceed

Exercise 102 – Couplets

1. friction; fiction
2. frightened; tightened
3. defect; effect
4. grovel; hovel
5. battle; cattle

Exercise 103 – The odd man out

1. volume, edition, book, poem, supplement
2. gynaecology, opthalmology, osteopathy, psychology, orthopaedics
3. Christmas, winter, summer, spring, autumn
4. barley, flour, rape, oats, wheat
5. cough, shout, shriek, exclaim, bellow
6. forest, wood, flower, copse, spinney
7. end, termination, interval, close, conclusion
8. purple, scarlet, turquoise, shadow, grey
9. story, tail, myth, legend, fable
10. discontent, wretched, miserable, low, mood

Exercise 104 – Anagrams

1. REITG
   MAGE
   BEAZR
   ONIL

2. SEUHO
   MCONOM
   TEAHH
   RKAP

3. ONOM
   RAST
   HLOSOC
   ECTOM

4. KOESAD
   ISMOT
   LANEC
   PADM

5. NUFYN
   VRAGE
   MOCIC
   NATIUQ

6. LARTWRE
   CTHAY
   ISPH
   RYORL

7. ERDAB
   NABNAA
   EAPR
   PELPA

8. OCLELGE
   SRYENRU
   LHNCPECTOIY
   INSTVERYUI

9. DIDBSTUH
   PSAITBT
   ITOCHALC
   TONPRTEAST

10. VNAY
    ULBE
    ITEHW
    ZRUAE

Exercise 105 – Confusable words

1. She returned . . . car. *(there, their)*
2. The . . . ran for two years. *(cereal, serial)*
3. Earlier this morning she was in . . . pain. *(terrible, chronic)*
4. What was your . . . when you were away yesterday? *(excuse, alibi)*
5. . . . than five people applied. *(less, fewer)*
6. They . . . not have come, had they not been forced to. *(may, might)*
7. I want to . . . down. *(lay, lie)*
8. I . . . in the garden all afternoon. *(lay, laid)*
9. Opinion . . . are rarely accurate. *(polls, poles)*
10. I don't have much . . . in this. *(practise, practice)*

Exercise 106 – Making words

1. Ph
2. Ma
3. Bi
4. Es
5. Wo
6. Ap
7. Gu
8. Ce
9. Su
10. It

Exercise 107 – Antonyms

1. Democracy   D. . . . . .p
2. Auspicious   O. . . . .s
3. Ignite   E. . . . . . . .h
4. Proceed   P. . . .e
5. Open   R. . . . . .d
6. Punish   C. . . . .e
7. Benefit   D. . . . . .e
8. Inflexible   M. . . . . . .e
9. Confident   B. l
10. Worldly   N. . .e

Exercise 108 – Words with more than one meaning

1. employer (. . . . . .) learn
2. row (. . . . .) wander
3. pair (. . . . . .) link
4. proper (. . . . . . .) rectify
5. beak (. . . .) invoice
6. strike (. . .) success
7. esteem (. . . . .) increase
8. low (. . . .) feathers
9. description (. . . . .) painting of person
10. unspecific (. . . . . . .) military officer

Exercise 109 – Find the word ending

1. G   2. C
    F   R
    BR   W
    M   ...   ST   ...
    H   M
    ST   B
    W   S

3.	B		7.	D	
	CL			THR	
	D			L	
	GL	...		G	...
	M			H	
	W			DR	
	L			CH	
4.	M		8.	TW	
	B			N	
	CH			R	
	S	...		L	...
	P			D	
	W			V	
	L			M	
5.	S		9.	B	
	TH			L	
	K			W	
	R	...		S	...
	L			D	
	P			T	
	W			V	
6.	Y		10.	W	
	B			R	
	D			H	
	LE	...		KN	...
	E			ST	
	YE			E	
	T			P	

Exercise 110 – The nearest definition

1. PROTOCOL: (a) original draft of diplomatic document. (b) etiquette. (c) peasants. (d) manners.
2. UMBRAGE: (a) shadow. (b) small umbrella. (c) sense of injury. (d) type of cloud.
3. OLIGARCHY: (a) small democratic state. (b) republic. (c) state

governed by a small group of people. (d) state governed by a large group of people.

4. LORE: (a) knowledge on a subject. (b) expression of surprise. (c) old law. (d) expression.
5. CURTAIL: (a) cut off. (b) cut short. (c) long curtain. (d) prevent.
6. CAUCUS: (a) group. (b) local political party committee. (c) meeting. (d) white person.
7. MAGNATE: (a) type of magnet. (b) successful businessman. (c) successful man. (d) eminent or wealthy man.
8. PARTISAN: (a) adherent to party or cause. (b) follower. (c) type of cheese. (d) politically ambitious person.
9. JAMBOREE: (a) gathering. (b) celebration. (c) family reunion. (d) percussion instrument.
10. COMPOUND: (a) combination. (b) substance. (c) mixture of several ingredients. (d) combined effort.

Exercise 111 – Find the rhyme

1. Blemish, chain = S...n
2. Soak, blood = F...d
3. Ceremony, kite = R..e
4. Fate, room = D..m
5. Dusk, skylight = T......t
6. Criticism, slack = F..k
7. Relative, creation = R......n
8. Real, factual = A....l
9 Matrimony, carriage = M......e
10. Austere, aesthetic = A.....c

Exercise 112 – Find the hidden word

1. The star romantically reminded me of home.
2. Wet roubles should never be used.
3. I like endings that make me laugh.
4. My kith and kin never meet.
5. I am glad letters are now arriving.

64

6. Strip everything away.
7. The tap languished unrepaired.
8. Find and pick learning from the trees.
9. Two hippopotamuses wallowed luxuriously.
10. Lava poured down from the volcano.

Exercise 113 – Synonyms

1.	Majestic	A....t
2.	Hate	L....e
3.	Commission	A.......e
4.	Slander	M....n
5.	Pamper	C....t
6.	Hillock	M...d
7.	Augment	S........t
8.	Sight	V....n
9.	Diet	B..t
10.	Irregular	E.....c

Exercise 114 – Mischmasch

1.	tio	6	ffe
2.	rys	7.	cst
3.	mic	8.	rge
4.	hth	9.	atc
5.	oin	10.	rou

Exercise 115 – Single words

1. The foreigner has become *a citizen of this country*. (adj.)
2. She has a *simple, unaffected* manner.
3. The two roads *cross each other* at this point.
4. She is *able to write with both her left and right hand.*
5. Charles Darwin shocked the world by his discoveries about *the origin and development of mankind.*

6. It is a *tiny village with no church.*
7. They have been arrested for *unlawfully intruding on his land.*
8. His attitude has been somewhat *offhand and supercilious.*
9. She looked *unmoved and indifferent* throughout.
10. Since the death of his wife he has *lived like an automaton.*

Exercise 116 – What's the difference?

1. Prejudice; preconception
2. Manners; etiquette
3. Binary; tertiary
4. Link; join
5. Sample; example
6. Testify; witness
7. Credit; merit
8. Lecture; preach
9. Reverie; dream
10. Monument; memorial

Exercise 117 – The linking word

1. ac(. . .)imetre
2. ar(. . .)dy
3. rab(. . .)ter
4. t(. . .)en
5. by(. . .)age
6. f(. . . .)ing
7. cut(. . .)ter
8. wal(. . .)meg
9. f(. . .)oon
10. wel(. . . .)ly

Exercise 118 – Doublets

1. Change *pick* into *drop*.
2. Change *all* into *few*.
3. Change *pool* into *lake*.
4. Change *rich* into *poor*.
5. Change *why* into *how*.

Exercise 119 – Test your understanding

1. trick; bamboozle
2. filibuster; debate
3. schoolboy; bumptious
4. ingenuous; comment
5. terrace; balustrade
6. swain; attentive
7. stomach; pancreas
8. opaque; obscure
9. appearance; dishevelled
10. eat; glutton

How *not* to improve your wordpower

REDUNDANT WORDS AND PHRASES

As well as thinking of ways to strengthen your wordpower, it is a good idea to think of the words and phrases that weaken your verbal skills. Only by eradicating these can you hope to speak and write fluently. There are countless examples of words and phrases which mean very little, but are simply used to fill out a sentence. The trouble with this 'padding' language is that it weakens the words which do have meaning. *At the end of the day, in the event, and so on and so forth* are the weeds in the garden of language; destructive, tenacious and only got rid of by thorough uprooting. The following list of sentences each contains an italicized redundant word or phrase. In each case the 'padding' adds nothing to the sense.

No, I'm *actually* catching the two o'clock train.

This is perhaps, *arguably*, the best wine I've ever tasted.

I don't like garlic *as such*.

Housewives are unpaid servants, *at the end of the day*.

At this moment in time we are currently expanding the firm.

I think you ought to tell him, *basically*.

Broadly speaking, she deserves more credit, really.

I'm in favour of it, *by and large*.

It's a *comparatively* real possibility, considering the circumstances this time.

I promise you that I'm *definitely* interested.

If you like, it is the writer's most famous book.

It's *in a way* an unusual house.

The main debate is *in essence* what we must attend to carefully.

I would like to say that *in the event* the situation is now critical.

Yes, he is a teacher, *in fact*.

We conclude that *in the final analysis* changes must be made.

The sum was *in the order of* £3,000 approximately.

In terms of behaviour, he is very naughty. [Instead of *as for*]

It's a *kind of* shop that looks like a house.

He made some *meaningful* comments during the meeting which were valuable.

I don't *necessarily* think that she's responsible this time.

I *personally* don't agree.

This offer guarantees a *real* transformation of your life!

He was a *relatively* old man.

Mr and Mrs James are *respectively* accountants.

It's a delay *situation*.

We have a *sort of* garden, only it's very overgrown.

I would not put any *undue* pressure on him yet.

It was *virtually* a near disaster.

He arrived at *what can only be described as* a critical stage.

They must go to the root of the problem, *when all's said and done*.

May I point out, *you know*, that it's already six o'clock?

In every example the sentence would be better without the redundant word or phrase. Exercise 120 (over the page) has much verbiage which needs eradicating; read the passage and then re-write it without all the 'padding'.

Exercise 120 – Redundant words and phrases

Basically, education is about preparing children for the adult world, if you like. By and large this means teaching children reading, writing, numeracy and so on and so forth, and teaching them how to behave towards others as such. Arguably, this kind of education of the heart is in a way much more difficult than the education of basic skills. For in the final analysis what are the values of our society that we are to teach our children? When all's said and done, we can no longer call ourselves a Christian society, for few people know anything about the Bible, at the end of the day. This is arguably the greatest problem for teachers at this moment in time. In the event, many of them are helpless when confronted by those ethical "Why?" questions which the young are wont to spring upon their elders. The sort of questions I mean are those in the order of "Why is marriage sacred if most parents seem to be divorced?" or "If God is love, why does He allow human suffering to continue?". These are comparatively difficult questions to answer, and may only be answered if the person asked inhabits a world of meaningful values to which he can refer.

CLICHÉS

Clichés do not give a good impression. Because they have been exhausted through overuse they tend to sound superficial and inadequate when something serious is trying to be said. However, not to use clichés can entail longwinded explanations; try saying *He got himself into a rut* in fewer words. But in the clichés listed below there are certainly other words and expressions that can do their job better. Rewrite the following clichés (shown in italics):

Exercise 121 – Clichés

1. Approaching him is a completely different *ball game.*
2. I would like to *draw a veil* over that part of the evening.
3. The *climate of opinion* favours the senior woman.
4. I shouldn't think people would, *in this day and age.*
5. That car is as *old as the hills.*
6. It is just the *tip of the iceberg* of the problem.
7. He was always *up with the lark.*
8. She was *green with envy* at his success.
9. I'm going to *leave no stone unturned* in discovering the truth.
10. *At this moment in time* I'm in a meeting.

THE VERBAL HURDLE

It is a good rule always to choose active verbs rather than passive verbs, adjectives, abstract nouns or adverbs, when you possibly can. When properly used, verbs are the most direct part of speech, yet so much of the way we use language now depends heavily on adverbs, adjectives and passive verbs. Take for example:

The project was *challenging* to all of us.

If you make the adjective *challenging* into an active verb, the sense has much more force and immediacy:

The project *challenged* all of us.

Another example:

He behaved *embarrassingly* towards them.

When you change the adverb *embarrassingly* into a verb the meaning is much more direct:

He *embarrassed* them.

In the following sentences, change the italicized words into active verbs:

Exercise 122 – The verbal hurdle

1. I find him *frightening.*
2. All the family *were charmed* by her.
3. What I find *striking* is their courage.
4. A model has been *constructed* by the firm.
5. The train made a *loop* round the mountain.
6. We found her remarks very *hurtful.*
7. *Regrettably*, they must refuse.
8. I feel great *admiration* for your work.
9. I found it a *liberating* experience.
10. He had been *tamed* by her into submission.

MORE EXERCISES ON PRECEDING POINTS

Exercise 123 – Redundant words and phrases

Remove the redundant words and phrases from the following passage:

By and large dieting is something that all young women think about, even though, at the end of the day, it is rarely necessary for them. The diet is a craze which can only be described as an obsession with achieving the perfect shape, which, in the event, is not an objective fact. In a way excessive concern about what you eat is in fact an excuse for thinking excessively about yourself; in other words it is arguably a manifestation of vanity.

But we must also consider the dieting phenomenon in terms of peer group pressure which basically can dictate to someone how they should look and behave. In the final analysis this is the problem situation. When all's said and done women shouldn't feel bullied by their more obsessive peers to feel obliged to eat only in the order of a few miserable number of calories per day. The pitiable thing is that so many women definitely do suffer this undue pressure, through friends and fashion magazines.

Being thin is a relatively modern sort of fashion – virtually no (or very few) women in the 1950s thought it desirable to rediscover their pre-pubescent shape. Speaking for myself, although at this moment in time I admit a faint dissatisfaction with my disproportionate bottom half, at the end of the day I personally would not swap my child-bearing hips for that unnaturally streamlined look.

Exercise 124 – Clichés
Rewrite the following clichés:

1. The story is lost *in the mists of time.*
2. She joined the *rat race*, like her friends.
3. He was the *life and soul* of the party.
4. The lorry *ground to a halt.*
5. The children were found *safe and sound* after their ordeal.
6. I'm working at it *slowly but surely.*
7. Avoid clichés *like the plague!*
8. That dog is as *ugly as sin.*
9. He is now *as blind as a bat.*
10. He kept *as cool as a cucumber.*

Exercise 125 – The verbal hurdle
Change the italicized words into active verbs:

1. He thought the music was *electrifying.*
2. They place great *reliance* on him.
3. The need to raise money *was discussed* by the committee.
4. That's how we were, *drifting* from one place to the next.
5. I *was introduced* by the hostess.
6. She was *argumentative* with everyone.
7. The *expresion* on his face was absolute horror.
8. The painter had now *been forgotten* by the public.
9. I get *tired* with all this physical work.
10. Once again, there's been a *failure* to communicate on his part.

Exercise 126 – Clichés

1. Poetry is *alive and well* in this country.
2. He droned on and on *ad nauseam.*
3. This is a real *bone of contention* between them.
4. *The powers that be* have forbidden that.
5. Those *halcyon days* are long past.
6. Please don't *take it to heart.*
7. They supported us *through thick and thin.*
8. He was always *building castles in Spain.*
9. I wish he wouldn't *chop and change* all the time.
10. She looked as *pretty as a picture.*

Exercise 127 – The verbal hurdle

1. I left, *creeping* on all fours.
2. I now feel *inspired* by that book to go travelling.
3. He then had to make his *interpretation* differently.
4. You must have a great *understanding* of other people.
5. For them it was a *reminder* of the past.
6. What a *flourishing* girl, compared with last year!
7. After such a long time, he found their affection *touching.*
8. She *had a dream* about her childhood home.
9. The pressure was becoming increasingly *intense* throughout the week.
10. She was *impressed* by his grasp of the facts.

Answers to exercises

Exercise 1

1. Spy 2. Shock 3. Clear 4. Roomy 5. Battle 6. Avert
7. Curb 8. Levy 9. Teem 10. Feat

Exercise 2

1. hear, heart 2. add, madden 3. hoe, father 4. sap, leaf, fort, forth 5. scar, scarlet 6. brain, rain 7. clever, ever 8. triple, sty 9. advent, adventure, sop 10. want, wan

Exercise 3

1. Timid 2. Pleasure 3. Shape 4. Alter 5. Riddle 6. Furious
7. Rarely 8. Sunrise 9. Courageous 10. Package

Exercise 4

1. advantage 2. intimacy 3. lukewarm, tepid 4. alternating
5. patricide/parricide 6. qualms 7. cowardly about *(note the changed preposition)* 8. moderately 9. recline 10. sordid

Exercise 5

1. silhouette 2. fiction 3. stampede 4. nutrient 5. whiff
6. etymology 7. hurdle 8. hypnotic 9. trilogy 10. regulation

Exercise 6

1. Both words say something about ability. A capable person is able; an efficient person is thorough and competent, as well as able.
2. An energetic person may not be good at sports, like an athletic person. But he will have plenty of energy for other pursuits.

3. Things are deceptive and people are deceitful: *His smile was deceptive; he was a deceitful man.*
4. Something that irritates you is annoying; something that exasperates you is intensely annoying.
5. Labour generally means physical exertion, whereas work can mean both physical and mental exertion.
6: Someone who is taught lacks a skill. Someone who is instructed may lack part of the skill, or may simply be fulfilling commands.
7. You may comply with something (act in accordance with a wish or command), while disagreeing with it. If you agree with something you fully support it.
8. A lazy person does not want to exert himself. A languid person thinks he is unable to.
9. A poignant story evokes even greater sympathy and feeling than a moving story.
10. A cold woman might succumb to a man's charms, but not a frigid woman.

Exercise 7

1. men 2. fall 3. care 4. bond 5. rough 6. ass 7. main
8. sign 9. use 10. gin

Exercise 8

1. mugwump 2. Eurobond, cement 3. at this moment in time
4. Imparadised in one another's arms (*Milton*) 5. opthalmology

Exercise 9

1.	FIND	2.	MOTHER
	BIND		BROTHER
	BOND		BATHER
	BONE		FATHER
	LONE		
	LOSE		

3. DRY	5. ILL
WRY	ALL
WAY	ALE
SAY	ALT
SAT	AIT
SET	FIT
WET	

4. SEA
   SET
   LET
   LEY
   LAY
   SAY
   SKY

Exercise 10

1. Protected species are animals under the threat of extinction.
2. The suspect is being kept under surveillance.
3. The obsequious dog crawled to its master.
4. Your sophistry does not persuade me.
5. Nobody knew of the clandestine conspiracy.
6. Will this nostrum cure my complaint?
7. The subject is too recondite for most people.
8. Nobody supported their faction.
9. The parents did not consent to the marriage.
10. The proselyte was converted from his old faith.

Exercise 11

1. effect 2. appreciative 3. canvas 4. dependent 5. uninterested
6. flout 7. intense 8. masterly 9. precipitous 10. seasonal

Exercise 12

1. *Churchill.*
   (All the others are poets: *Keats, Byron, Chaucer.*)

2. *Lily.*
   (All the others are trees: *oak, beech, lime.*)
3. *Violin.*
   (All the others are wind instruments: *flute, oboe, clarinet.*)
4. *Train.*
   (All the others are motor vehicles: *van, bus, lorry.*)
5. *Spain.*
   (All the others are capital cities: *Paris, Madrid, Rome.*)
6. *Dentist.*
   (All the others are members of the legal profession: *judge, barrister, solicitor.*)
7. *House.*
   (All the others are pieces of furniture: *chair, table, stool.*)
8. *Study.*
   (All the others are sports: *tennis, polo, rugby.*)
9. *Wallet.*
   (All the others are clothes: *vest, trousers, blouse.*)
10. *Priest.*
    (All the others are shopkeepers: *grocer, tailor, baker.*)

Exercise 13

1. protected 2. piano 3. flavour 4. damage 5. mosque
6. attractive 7. fern 8. interesting 9. inundate 10. pour

Exercise 14

1. numen, train, meant, mutter, taint, entrust, lute, trial, alter, treat.
2. vary, vase, yarn, earns, rave, saver, area, sear, vine, sinner.
3. stint, stable, lament, bestial, enmesh, mental, behest, taint, neat, taste.
4. bray, phobia, hog, grab, graph, big, rag, yap, hob, orgy.
5. lower, crawl, cruel, flour, careful, rifle, flea, awful, cower, callow.
6. pence, prove, drive, pride, cover, price, niece, voice, drone, deed.

7. tine, toe, shine, shoe, hit, then, thin, nest, shout, net.
8. rout, thought, gout, hug, thorough, gut, trout, tutu, root, tort.
9. sum, muse, nose, some, cue, use, one, scone, scum, come.
10. count, nonce, none, tun, neat, ounce, nut, ace, tenon, cant.

Exercise 15

1. I've tried, but failed, to play a tune/With a knife, a fork and a wooden spoon.
2. Come, madam, let us enjoy the spree/And spread the picnic beneath this tree.
3. I must plead and I must coax/For already she thinks it is a hoax.
4. Oh no! I've found the pony lame/He can't be in the gymkhana game.
5. If you are a walker and a rambler/It's most unlikely you're also a gambler.

Exercise 16

1. Inarticulate   2. Listless   3. Introvert   4. Organized
5. Irreligious   6. Unfeeling   7. Partial   8. Hopeless
9. Inopportune 10. Uncertain

Exercise 17

1. ale 2. ight 3. eed 4. est 5. ile 6. ate 7. ipe 8. ade
9. ime 10. out

Exercise 18

1. well 2. roll 3. rock 4. wreck 5. charm 6. current
7. approach 8. charge 9. private 10. cry

Exercise 19

1. Perjury 2. Dirge 3. Guise 4. Expedient 5. Style 6. Contagious 7. Reduce 8. Harrowing 9. Jaded 10. Whim

Exercise 20

1. estrange(d), ranged 2. human 3. functional, splay(s), sup
4. comely, replay 5. roundabout, sew, frock(s) 6. toe(d), editor
7. hew, sallow, allow 8. perjury 9. there, earth, earthern, art
10. hem, helmet, met, mete, meter

Exercise 21

1. Column 2. Strength 3. Unexpected 4. Target
5. Frank 6. Bough 7. Lukewarm 8. Establish 9. Early
10. Ultimate

Exercise 22

1. pristine 2. stigma 3. magnanimous 4. misogyny
5. persecuted 6. dais 7. franchise 8. fillip 9. radiant
10. deployed

Exercise 23

1. vacuum 2. mission 3. agree 4. igneous 5. rococo
6. sneeze 7. paradox 8. slipshod 9. garbled 10. radius

Exercise 24

1. You can both undo and untie a parcel, but you can only *undo* somebody else's work.
2. Barbaric is a more pejorative word than primitive. Primitive people may not belong to the modern world but they do not behave like savages, like barbaric people.

3. Succeed is a more specific word than achieve. *She succeeded in passing the exam, and so achieved her great ambition.*
4. You can avoid all sorts of things, but you can only bypass an obstruction, be it a town or malfunctioning cardiac valve.
5. To defend something suggests that it is under attack. To protect something means more generally to keep it safe.
6. Sufficient means enough, whereas ample means abundant.
7. Something that is excruciating is worse than painful; it is agonizing.
8. Friends may have different political beliefs, but comrades share the same socialist beliefs.
9. A superior mind has greater intellectual powers than the average. A supercilious mind believes itself superior and looks down on others.
10. An ambiguous or equivocal remark has more than one meaning. An equivocal person is a suspicious character.

Exercise 25

1. hat 2. brow 3. right 4. utter 5. out 6. possess 7. red 8. tend 9. test 10. gain

Exercise 26

1. Star Wars 2. at the end of the day 3. mummy 4. computer 5. fridge

Exercise 27

1.	2.
HARD	WHITE
HART	WRITE
TART	TRITE
TORT	TRICE
SORT	TRICK
SOOT	BRICK
SOFT	BROCK
	BLOCK
	BLACK

3.	EVIL	4.	TREE
	VILE		FREE
	WILE		FRET
	WILD		FEET
	WOLD		FEED
	WOOD		HEED
	GOOD		HOED
			HOOD
			WOOD

5. TELL
    TALL
    TALE
    TAME
    TIME

Exercise 28

1. Lambs are said to gambol in the spring.
2. His mordant sarcasm was unattractive.
3. How can we solve this intractable problem?
4. The menagerie was full of exotic animals.
5. His sense of guilt filled him with contrition.
6. The hierarchy of the firm is strict.
7. My blunder caused endless raillery.
8. Hypnosis is said to cure certain addictions.
9. Employees received gratuities according to their performance.
10. At the beginning of the play the hero soliloquizes.

Exercise 29

1. negligible 2. luxurious 3. punctilious 4. tortuous 5. turgid
6. resort 7. practicable 8. judicious 9. magnitude
10. infer.

Exercise 30

1. *Student*
   (All the others are professionals: *doctor, teacher, lawyer*.)

2. *Garden.*
    (All the others are houses: *bungalow, apartment, mansion.*)
3. *Easter.*
    (All the others are seasons: *winter, spring, autumn.*)
4. *Flour.*
    (All the others are types of grain: *barley, wheat, oats.*)
5. *Silver.*
    (All the others are precious stones: *ruby, sapphire, emerald.*)
6. *Wind.*
    (All the others are types of weather: *snow, hail, sleet.*)
7. *Ankle.*
    (All the others are parts of the face: *chin, cheeks, eyebrow.*)
8. *Giraffe.*
    (All the others are insects: *louse, beetle, centipede.*)
9. *India.*
    (All the others are nationalities: *French, Italian, Belgian.*)
10. *Dickens.*
    (All the others are composers: *Beethoven, Bach, Brahms.*)

Exercise 31

1. embarrassing   2. exacting   3. country   4. crowd   5. converse
6. possess   7. drive   8. reconciliation   9. begin   10. extraneous

Exercise 32

1. part, apart, trap, pip, trip, ran, nip, pit, pan, tin.
2. wit, thaw, drawl, withdraw, halt, hilt, wild, hail, laid, withal.
3. rent, ague, mean, urge, rate, tear, near, argue, rant, runt.
4. rude, grit, tide, grate, guide, aide, great, drag, dirge, urge.
5. tear, aunt, pint, rope, meat, pore, trap, patient, pattern, train.
6. `ardent, rant, year, order, torrid, dairy, aorta, entry, exit, tarry.
7. gate, prop, agate, taper, part, paper, peat, grate, groat, trope.
8. whip, pew, ripe, whisp, hip, pie, whir, ship, rise, wise.
9. turn, venture, advert, advent, denture, nave, read, tread, tend,
    rat, nerve.
10. gauge, gage, ague, lean, lag, lunge, gag, glean, élan, ale.

Exercise 33

1. Is it a gaggle, a brace, a herd,/Or a covey, a shoal — what is that word?
2. When born we are unwillingly hurled/Into this dark and cruel world.
3. The hen has laid/So the bills can be paid.
4. Given any excuse she would start to chatter,/But never revealed what was really the matter.
5. How can we be happy? How can we be blithe?/When death is lurking near with his fatal scythe?

Exercise 34

1. Apathy   2. Obedient   3. Obese   4. Strong   5. Injustice   6. Candid   7. Prudent   8. Deteriorate   9. Follower   10. Extraordinary.

Exercise 35

1. eam   2. ass   3. amp   4. ane   5. one   6. ool   7. ump   8. eat   9. int   10. ame

Exercise 36

1. start   2. rule   3. shape   4. base   5. plain   6. advance   7. grace   8. lie   9. fare   10. gloom

Exercise 37

1. dense   2. laughter, aught   3. drape, draper(y), sand   4. ley, fan   5. confront(s), sup, heal   6. peeling   7. twill, urn   8. remember(s), stake   9. eschew(ed), theme   10. dozen

Exercise 38

1. Irritable   2. Charm   3. Meeting   4. Paragon   5. Bewilder   6. Decrease   7. Shared   8. Hoist   9. Fickle   10. Exuberant

Exercise 39

1. fulsome   2. panacea   3. tendentious   4. impresario
5. internecine   6. arboretum   7. recidivist   8. autobiography
9. symphony   10. sententiousness.

Exercise 40

1. absurd   2. mattock   3. ribbon   4. slogan   5. scalp
6. chrome   7. obdurate   8. biography   9. cardinal   10. juggernaut

Exercise 41

1. A trivial objection is unimportant. A frivolous objection is both
    unimportant and irreverent.
2. An aggressive person is not necessarily violent, but a violent
    person must be aggressive.
3. Rancour is a more extreme and long-established form of
    bitterness.
4. People make plans and governments make policies.
5. Relevant and germane mean the same, but an issue that is
    germane must be germane *to* something else.
6. Bullish is generally confined to describing the financial market.
    If the market is bullish it means that a spirit of optimism prevails,
    making share prices increase.
7. A chronology describes a sequence of events in the order that
    they occurred. A history does not necessarily relate events in their
    chronological order.
8. A review of company management suggests that the pre-existing
    system is already understood. An inquiry into the management
    suggests that little or nothing is known about it beforehand.
9. A vocation for a profession is the feeling a person has that he is
    suited to the career. When he takes it up it is his occupation.
10. Ingenuous means primarily open and frank, for example *an
    ingenuous remark*, although it also suggests innocence.

Exercise 42

1. read   2. port   3. ore   4. duct   5. quest   6. light   7. pen   8. shall
9. gest   10. wake

Exercise 43

1. Give yourself time to stand and stare!   2. caring capitalism
3. tintinabulation   4. oleander   5. gossamer

Exercise 44

1.	HEAD	2.	WORK
	LEAD		PORK
	LOAD		PERK
	GOAD		PERT
	GOOD		PEST
	FOOD		REST
	FOOT		

3.	TAME	4.	LOVE
	TIME		HOVE
	TILE		HAVE
	WILE		HATE
	WILD		

5. RISE
   RASE
   BASE
   BALE
   BALL
   FALL

Exercise 45

1. With the plan scotched, it is impossible to continue.
2. The headmistress gave a homily about helping others.
3. The conversation was so desultory that we never discussed anything properly.
4. The draconian laws placed more restrictions on the country.
5. Nobody believes this apocryphal story.
6. A kangeroo is a marsupial.
7. A sinecure is a job which exists in name only.

8. He always writes under a pseudonym.
9. Who was your precursor in the company?
10. His gratuitous remarks were irritating.

Exercise 46

1. new 2. complaisant 3. continual 4. distinguished
5. imminent 6. immigrants 7. contemptible 8. alternative
9. benevolent 10. titillating

Exercise 47

1. *Compass.*
   (All the others are shapes: *square, triangle, circle.*)
2. *Chicken.*
   (All the others are puddings: *crumble, tart, sorbet.*)
3. *Paint*
   (All the others are colours: *green, yellow, black.*)
4. *Australia.*
   (All the others are European countries: *Greece, Holland, Germany.*)
5. *Present.*
   (All the others are illnesses: *headache, influenza, fever.*)
6. *Death.*
   (All the others are crimes: *theft, murder, fraud.*)
7. *Studio.*
   (All the others are entertainments: *concert, film, play.*)
8. *Church.*
   (All the others are to do with water: *river, lake, stream.*)
9. *Copper.*
   (All the others are fabrics: *cotton, corduroy, silk.*)
10. *Touch.*
    (All the others are facial expresisons: *grimace, smile, frown.*)

Exercise 48

1. absolute 2. instruction 3. sanctimonious 4. care 5. injure
6. sleepy 7. medium 8. forgive 9. argue 10. revision

Exercise 49

1. note, rote, tore, tire, inter, iron, tea, tier, rent, rein.
2. sod, trod, rout, toss, dour, rust, astir, dais, truss, staid.
3. grove, pose, grave, seep, pore, progress, reeve, sieve, give, press.
4. fate, ague, gait, gate, fuge, fat, gut, get, fit, feat.
5. heat, meat, haste, meant, shunt, mint, seat, hate, site, sane.
6. queen, chin, quit, quiet, quench, cheque, niece, net, chit, hen.
7. price, piece, niece, trace, trice, pine, pane, taper, caper, preen.
8. charter, heart, strict, cheat, hatter, hectic, terse, chatter, stitch, starch.
9. poach, roach, rope, hare, harp, hoar, pore, pare, chore, hope.
10. nail, prison, lesion, reason, poison, rifle, frisson, nasal, loose, felon.

Exercise 50

1. /That he had a million pounds concealed.   2. /There will be time to find a mate.   3. /While the English are either too quiet or too loud. 4. /Why haven't you smiled since we were wed? 5. /Which is highly dangerous, my doctor says.

Exercise 51

1. Republic 2. Philanthropic 3. Unstable 4. Serene 5. Understated 6. Senior 7. Parched 8. Insufficient 9. Reticent 10. Circumspect

Exercise 52

1. unt   2. are   3. own   4. eep   5. ing   6. age   7. oon   8. ear 9. oot   10. ack

Exercise 53

1. end   2. poor   3. fair   4. true   5. strike   6. contest   7. purse 8. pass   9. press   10. habit

Exercise 54

1. (c) play on words   2. (a) hold opinion   3. (b) particular   4. (d) out of date   5. (b) burning, corroding substance   6. (c) feat of endurance   7. (c) at point of death   8. (a) commonplace   9. (c) tear limbs from   10. (d) resembling ancestors

Exercise 55

1. Taper   2. Devise   3. Grapple   4. Jar   5. Supine
6. Debilitate   7. Halter   8. Complete   9. Grave   10. Ornate

Exercise 56

1. free, frank, fry, friction, frisson, from, fraction, frond, fright, frolic.
2. able, absolute, abacus, abominable, abysmal, abandon, abduct, abscond, about, absent.
3. pot, pout, ponder, pound, postulate, poodle, post, pond, poison, poignant.
4. spasm, space, spin, spot, splinter, speak, splutter, spend, spade, special.
5. mile, middle, mixture, mint, mitre, mischief, midget, miss, mistake, misnomer.
6. week, weak, wet, weather, wean, wedding, west, weep, weird, welcome.
7. mystery, myopia, myth, myrrh, myself, myrtle, myriad, mycosis, myosotis, myrmidon.
8. done, doe, doctor, dogged, donor, dominate, doll, doom, door, double.
9. runner, rumour, rude, rustic, rubber, rubicund, rumble, ruin, rupee, ruthless.
10. ski, skeleton, skill, skewer, skate, skin, skirmish, skittish, sky, skipper.

Exercise 57

1. impatient(ly)   2. wither, hero, herb   3. passage, sage   4. season
5. arch   6. scream   7. hold   8. bustle   9. carp, carpet   10. resign

Exercise 58

1. Exact   2. Calculating   3. Congenial   4. Precarious   5. Hesitant
6. Veil   7. Ostracize   8. Submit   9. Petrify   10. Bequeath

Exercise 59

1. jejune   2. peccadillo   3. extract   4. cadaverous   5. random
6. intuition   7. ledger   8. prior   9. pillar   10. stratagem

Exercise 60

1. Kings and queens reign, and all other leaders rule.
2. There are never more than two alternatives, but there can be any number of options.
3. Someone who is fastidious is even harder to please than the particular person.
4. To swear to do something means to promise on oath to do it.
5. Both words mean emitting light, but when used figuratively, only looks can be radiant and only ideas can be bright.
6. A capricious person is unpredictable. A volatile person is changeable and flighty.
7. Being solicitous about something means feeling very concerned about it. It can also mean being eager to do something, which being concerned does not necessarily suggest.
8. Siesta is a more specific word than rest. It means a rest in the afternoon.
9. Rough and coarse may both be used to describe surfaces and textures. In describing behaviour, rough suggests disorderliness and even violence, whereas coarse suggests vulgarity and lack of refinement.
10. An annual plant lasts for one year only, while a perennial plant lasts for several years. (Annual comes from *annus*, the Latin word for year. Perennial means literally *through the year*.)

Exercise 61

1. transmogrified   2. epicene   3. indentures   4. indictment
5. endemic 6. sepoys 7. semantic 8. cowl 9. senile 10. Post Restante

Exercise 62

1. nest 2. edge 3. ape 4. king 5. way 6. pear 7. own 8. lack
9. car 10. top

Exercise 63

1. The hooligans were always caught/However much they kicked and fought.
2. See where it is, that happy hole/Where Pyramus Thisbe's kisses stole.
3. The costume assistant has sewn the last stitch/So may the play run now without a hitch.
4. What a precarious thing is fame/It will either mend, or it will maim.
5. The escape has been botched/So the plan must be scotched.

Exercise 64

<table>
<tr><td>1.</td><td>GIVE</td><td>3.</td><td>WING</td></tr>
<tr><td></td><td>GAVE</td><td></td><td>RING</td></tr>
<tr><td></td><td>SAVE</td><td></td><td>RANG</td></tr>
<tr><td></td><td>SAKE</td><td></td><td>RANT</td></tr>
<tr><td></td><td>TAKE</td><td></td><td>WANT</td></tr>
<tr><td></td><td></td><td></td><td>WAIT</td></tr>
<tr><td></td><td></td><td></td><td>WAIL</td></tr>
<tr><td></td><td></td><td></td><td>TAIL</td></tr>
<tr><td>2.</td><td>DAWN</td><td>4.</td><td>CAT</td></tr>
<tr><td></td><td>DARN</td><td></td><td>COT</td></tr>
<tr><td></td><td>DARK</td><td></td><td>COG</td></tr>
<tr><td></td><td>BARK</td><td></td><td>DOG</td></tr>
<tr><td></td><td>BACK</td><td></td><td></td></tr>
<tr><td></td><td>BUCK</td><td></td><td></td></tr>
<tr><td></td><td>DUCK</td><td></td><td></td></tr>
<tr><td></td><td>DUSK</td><td></td><td></td></tr>
</table>

5. SHAME
   SHAKE
   SLAKE
   FLAKE
   FLAME
   BLAME

Exercise 65

1. Camellias flower in the spring.
2. The protestors heckled the speaker and interrupted the meeting.
3. This scandal has tarnished his once faultless reputation.
4. He played a piano sonata by Mozart.
5. Gargoyles leered from the roof of the cathedral.
6. Meritricious acts seek praise, but do not necessarily deserve it.
7. However much the cognoscenti praised the book, it did not sell well.
8. He knew his calling was to be a priest.
9. It was bracing weather on that December morning.
10. In the third Act of the opera the heroine dies.

Exercise 66

1. principle 2. formally 3. ingenious 4. list 5. array 6. plains
7. razed 8. cannon 9. waive 10. stationary

Exercise 67

1. *Film.*
   (All the others are written works: *novel, poem, essay.*)
2. *Rubber.*
   (All the others are stones: *brick, cement, marble.*)
3. *Cheque.*
   (All the others are types of currency: *lira, dollars, sterling.*)

92

4. *Shout.*
   (All the others are ways of laughing: *laugh, chuckle, giggle.*)
5. *Elbow.*
   (All the others are parts of the eye: *iris, pupil, retina.*)
6. *Friend.*
   (All the others are relatives: *niece, cousin, nephew.*)
7. *Horse.*
   (All the others are dogs: *poodle, alsatian, spaniel.*)
8. *Coat.*
   (All the others are luggage: *basket, satchel, suitcase.*)
9. *Year.*
   (All the others are to do with time: *minute, hour, second.*)
10. *Road.*
   (All the others are parts of a tree: *branch, trunk, twig.*)

Exercise 68

1. mode, mace, racy, ream, cream, yore, yard, dream, dram, mead.
2. trap, last, past, soap, oats, oast, pastor, salt, part, post.
3. may, yam, hog, agony, nag, gamy, ham, man, any, hag.
4. serve, veer, seer, sire, visor, verse, sieve, rove, error, river.
5. gave, gable, table, beat, leave, veal, able, gale, vale, bale.
6. cult, tall, cull, rat, rut, cat, cut, talc, curt, arc.
7. lost, gist, gilt, silt, salt, stag, goat, nag, glint, slant.
8. wolf, low, fell, well, flow, flew, owl, few, foe, woe.
9. rate, trace, rote, coat, treat, contact, tact, contract, conceal, nonce.
10. grave, rave, veer, verge, never, range, gear, raven, nave, near.

Exercise 69

1. Distinguished 2. Imitation 3. Humour 4. Go 5. Pedantic
6. Keep 7. Steeple 8. Acknowledge 9. Sea 10. Triple

Exercise 70

1. errand, erstwhile, err, erupt, erudite, erode, erratic, erect, ermine, erotic.
2. keen, ken, keep, kerb, kedgeree, keel, kestrel, kernel, kerchief, key.

3. butane, butcher, but, buxom, buy, button, buzzard, butter, busy, busker.
4. floor, flout, flavour, flat, flaccid, flannel, flame, flamboyant, flail, fleece.
5. osprey, oscillate, ostensible, ostentation, ostler, osteopathy, ostrich, ostinato, ossify, ostracize.
6. rate, ran, rain, range, rattle, rack, rapport, ration, raillery, rake.
7. inside, intend, intrude, investigate, intoxicate, invade, inhabit,
8. very, verisimilitude, verge, vermilion, verse, vent, verbal, veneer, verdict, vengeance.
9. graphic, green, grumble, gruel, grow, group, groom, grotesque, grip, grill.
10. embezzle, embroil, embed, employ, emperor, emulate, emerald, empty, empyrean, emigrate.

Exercise 71

1. Barren 2. Herbivore 3. Bosky 4. Villain 5. Liberate
6. Abnormal 7. Visitor 8. Nadir 9. Irreverent 10. Infrequent

Exercise 72

1. ite 2. ire 3. ower 4. ast 5. and 6. ong 7. ape 8. eer
9. ope 10. oat

Exercise 73

1. (b) garment for the dead 2. (b) sight 3. (c) trust in or reliance on
4. (a) something which completes 5. (b) legal trickery 6. (c) odd
7. (d) moral condition 8. (c) compulsory 9. (b) type of manuscript 10. (a) introductory performance, action, etc.

Exercise 74

1. change 2. frame 3. cheer 4. reel 5. desert 6. figure
7. board 8. right 9. contract 10. issue

Exercise 75

1. Selective 2. Assemble 3. React 4. Receptacle 5. Alter
6. Main 7. Grasp 8. Veil 9. Hectic 10. Myth

Exercise 76

1. sag, agree(d) 2. maid, fort, forth 3. tire(d) 4. blemish, plea
5. wince, soft 6. abbey 7. fade, edit(s) 8. renege 9. set, end, arch,
replay 10. shade

Exercise 77

1. Turgid 2. Comic 3. Rival 4. Sample 5. Decline 6. Manifest
7. Gambit 8. Stringent 9. Propound 10. Conundrum

Exercise 78

1. mischief 2. nowadays 3. factotum 4. explain 5. obstruct
6. distinguish 7. assumption 8. kindergarten 9. bridegroom
10. warmth

Exercise 79

1. Spartan 2. meanders 3. despotic 4. desultory 5. peninsula
6. sceptical 7. bridleway 8. martyr 9. quattro cento 10. estuary

Exercise 80

1. To embellish means to beautify, while to decorate means to adorn.
2. To lurk is a more threatening word than to hide: *He did not realize what terrors were lurking for him.*
3. A clever person is also intelligent, but an intelligent person is not necessarily clever. Cleverness suggests an aptitude that intelligence implies but does not assure.
4. Sensual denotes sexual and voluptuous sensations, which sensuous does not: *Music can be sensuous, while eating food can be sensual.*

5. Something that is cathartic purges, while something that is therapeutic heals.
6. Humid means moist, while wet suggests a further degree of dampness.
7. Remote has the further meaning of seclusion, for example *a remote village*.
8. Chance means good fortune, whereas luck can be good or bad.
9. People remove things, but depart from places.
10. A query expresses doubt or objection, which a question does not necessarily do.

Exercise 81

1. /I'd prefer some other recreation.   2. /Life for you holds only charm.   3. /To dine at eight o'clock tonight.   4. /(Have the Americans really bought her?)   5. /Why Christmas is called the festive season.

Exercise 82

1. work   2. lay   3. lame   4. round   5. tempt   6. ear   7. dress   8. room   9. ease   10. talk

Exercise 83

1. WORD
    WARD
    HARD
    HERD
    HEED
    DEED

2. BOOK
    COOK
    COOL
    POOL
    POLL
    PILL
    FILL
    FILM

3. BORN	5. WARM
BORE	WARD
WORE	LARD
WIRE	LORD
DIRE	FORD
DIRT	FOLD
DIET	COLD
DIED	

4. LOSS
   BOSS
   BASS
   BAST
   BAIT
   WAIT
   WAIN
   GAIN

Exercise 84

1. The bust is made of marble.
2. A ha-ha divides the garden from the parkland.
3. Some religions encourage fanatics more than others.
4. He has been canonized and is now known as 'Saint Peter'.
5. Small talk was anathema to him; he tended to leave the room when there was chat.
6. The artist paints best in oils.
7. Applicants must send a portfolio of their work.
8. His intransigence over this issue was very irritating.
9. The farmer is leaving the field fallow this year.
10. The usher showed us to our seats.

Exercise 85

1. fortuitous 2. besides 3. censored 4. deficient 5. deprecated
6. exhaustive 7. notable 8. observances 9. insidious 10. moor

Exercise 86

1. *Fight.*
   (All the others are aims: *aim, end, goal.*)
2. *Tortoise.*
   (All the others are rodents: *rodent, mouse, gerbil.*)
3. *Apple.*
   (All the others are dried fruits: *prune, sultana, currant.*)
4. *Neck.*
   (All the others are parts of the foot: *heel, sole, arch.*)
5. *Ride.*
   (All the others are ways of counting: *calculate, add, count.*)
6. *Baby.*
   (All the others are pairs or more of babies: *twins, quadruplets, triplets.*)
7. *Flower.*
   (All the others are types of wood: *walnut, mahogany, teak.*)
8. *Novel.*
   (All the others are types of speech: *dialogue, debate, talk.*)
9. *Plate.*
   (All the others are meals: *lunch, supper, breakfast.*)
10. *Play.*
    (All the others are ways of cheating: *trick, deceive, cheat.*)

Exercise 87

1. nephew   2. church   3. fishing   4. plea   5. floral   6. valley
7. speak   8. nose   9. shoe   10. fish

Exercise 88

1. gold, god, goal, gorilla, gong, good, gossamer, gourd, goitre, gondola.
2. civil, cicada, cite, cigar, citrus, cistern, citadel, citizen, circumference, cipher.
3. know, knack, knit, knife, knot, knuckle, knoll, knock, knave, knead.
4. tap, tackle, tassle, taper, table, taste, tabulate, talk, tango, tamper.
5. nuisance, number, nude, nugget, nurse, nurture, nun, nutrition, nucleus, nudge.
6. let, letter, lesson, leader, leak, leap, leech, leper, lethal, lechery.

7. roll, rose, rostrum, rot, roast, robber, rock, roe, roach, root.
8. jealous, jeep, jejune, jell, jeopardy, jet, jewel, jettison, jester, jeroboam.
9. quash, queen, query, quest, quagmire, quell, question, quill, quaff, quilt.
10. asp, asparagus, ashram, aspirate, ascertain, assail, asleep, assembly, astronomy, ashamed.

Exercise 89

1. Antisocial 2. Fake 3. Aimless 4. Calculated 5. Demented
6. Repellent 7. Casual 8. Philistine 9. Foolish 10. Hope

Exercise 90

1. ook 2. ove 3. ark 4. ine 5. ell 6. oom 7. art 8. ead
9. ing 10. ull

Exercise 91

1. trace 2. party 3. charge 4. want 5. brow 6. choice
7. spoke 8. cause 9. moving 10. pursuit

Exercise 92

1. (c) law students' debate 2. (b) medieval competition for noblemen
3. (b) gigantic wine bottle 4. (c) cap worn by Roman Catholic
clergymen 5. (d) penalty for disobedience 6. (a) ceremonial
washing 7. (b) result of preceding action 8. (d) type of lizard
9. (c) that can be touched or felt 10. (d) ceremonial sounding of
trumpets

Exercise 93

1. Tardy 2. Conceive 3. Daimon 4. Fortuitous 5. Minister
6. Grimace 7. Blanch 8. Diverting 9. Droll 10. Pate

Exercise 94

1. Cane 2. Tour 3. Haunt 4. Whimsy 5. Frivolous
6. Conspire 7. Constitute 8. Decoy 9. Charisma 10. Sleuth

Exercise 95

1. resist 2. cable, tear 3. better, let, swill 4. advice, sin(s)
5. meal 6. rice, mess 7. blow(er) 8. scrap(ped) 9. tale, tin
10. (a)broad, tin

Exercise 96

1. omniscient 2. rebellious 3. knowledge 4. already 5. concentrate 6. glimpse 7. pocket 8. fiasco 9. opportunity
10. undulate

Exercise 97

1. categorically 2. emasculating 3. quay 4. plantation
5. embargoed 6. pilgrimage 7. pageantry 8. dentures
9. bivouac 10. elocution

Exercise 98

1. To collaborate means to work together. To conspire means to plot secretly and for an unlawful purpose.
2. A cacophony is a discordant and disagreeable sound. Noises can be pleasant.
3. Diction is a more specific word than speech. It means the choice of words and phrases in speech or writing, or the manner of enunciation in speaking or singing.
4. The essence of something is defined, while its function is explained.

5. The derivation is the source and the origin is the root.
6. A sphere is a globe while a realm is a kingdom. Both can mean domain: *the heavenly sphere, the realm of poetry.*
7. Rebuke is a stronger form of reproof. Berate means simply to scold.
8. Things that are stylish are elegant and distinctive. Fashionable things do not always have these qualities.
9. An impressive house will inspire admiration. An imposing house inspires awe.
10. Terror is a feeling of extreme fear, while horror is a combination of fear and revulsion.

Exercise 99

1. press 2. grace 3. harm 4. claim 5. range 6. low
7. side 8. key 9. tract 10. ring

Exercise 100

1.	GAME	3.	FLOUR
	FAME		FLOOR
	FARE		FLOOD
	CARE		BLOOD
	CART		BROOD
	CAST		BROAD
	PAST		BREAD
	PEST		
	TEST		

		4.	WALK
2.	SLOW		WALL
	SLOT		WAIL
	SOOT		WAIT
	COOT		WRIT
	COST		GRIT
	CAST		GROT
	FAST		TROT

5. SOLO
    SILO
    SILT
    LILT
    LIST
    LUST
    DUST
    DUET

Exercise 101

1. The metals were melted in the crucible.
2. The priest was followed by his acolytes.
3. He accused me of being Laodicean in my opinions.
4. The headmaster was rhadamanthine in his punishment of wrongdoers.
5. A decision must be made; we must not procrastinate any furher.
6. He has been made curator of the museum.
7. Dyslexic children have greater problems with learning to read and write.
8. I don't understand that abstruse explanation.
9. As the factotum he managed all his master's affairs.
10. The cortège proceeded behind the coffin.

Exercise 102

1. Within the book world there's always friction/Between reviewers and writers of fiction.   2. The murderer cried 'Damn you all, I'm not frightened!'/As the noose round his neck was gradually tightened.   3. If it wasn't for the defect/The system would have had an effect.   4. It is outrageous that he should grovel/To be invited to live in that hovel.   5. The teacher said that at this battle/Instead of horses the troops rode cattle.

Exercise 103

1. poem   2. psychology   3. Christmas   4. flour   5. cough
6. flower   7. interval   8. shadow   9. tail   10. mood

Exercise 104

1. *Game.*
   (All the others are wild animals: *tiger, zebra, lion.*)
2. *House.*
   (All the others are types of open ground: *common, heath, park.*)
3. *School.*
   (All the others are heavenly bodies: *moon, star, comet.*)
4. *Clean.*
   (All the others are degrees of dampness: *soaked, moist, damp.*)
5. *Grave.*
   (All the others are ways of being amusing: *funny, comic, quaint.*)
6. *Lorry.*
   (All the others are sea-going vessels: *trawler, yacht, ship.*)
7. *Bread.*
   (All the others are fruits: *banana, pear, apple.*)
8. *Nursery.*
   (All the others are colleges: *college, polytechnic, university.*)
9. *Buddhist.*
   (All the others are Christians; *Baptist, Catholic, Protestant.*)
10. *White.*
    (All the others are blues: *navy, blue, azure.*)

Exercise 105

1. their   2. serial   3. terrible   4. alibi   5. fewer   6. might   7. lie
8. lay   9. polls   10. practice

Exercise 106

1. phenomenon, photograph, philanthrophy, phosphorus, physicist, phonetic, philander, philosopher, phlegm, phrase.
2. major, matter, map, mason, maple, massage, marauder, margin, material, mathematics.
3. bison, bicycle, biped, biscuit, bite, bivouac, bittern, bid, bitumen, biology.

4. esoteric, especial, escapade, eschatology, escort, espouse, essence, estate, esteem, essay.

5. worm, wood, wonder, woman, wombat, woe, wobble, wolf, woke, world.

6. appetite, appreciation, apple, apparent, apology, aphorism, apartment, ape, appoint, apostle.

7. guinea, guilt, guise, gut, guile, guess, guy, guru, gulf, gusto.

8. cereal, celandine, ceramic, cement, centre, ceremony, cerebral, centigrade, censure, cemetery.

9. sultana, suede, suave, sultry, suck, such, sunk, sundry, sumptuous, supernatural.

10. itinerant, itinerary, item, italic, itch, iterate, iterable, itself, Italophile, Italianate.

Exercise 107

1. Dictatorship 2. Ominous 3. Extinguish 4. Precede
5. Reserved 6. Condone 7. Disadvantage 8. Malleable
9. Bashful 10. Naive

Exercise 108

1. master 2. range 3. couple 4. correct 5. bill 6. hit
7. appreciate 8. down 9. portrait 10. general

Exercise 109

1. ood 2. ake 3. ean 4. ore 5. ick 6. arn 7. ive 8. ice
9. ent 10. ave

Exercise 110

1. (a) original draft of diplomatic document 2. (c) sense of injury
3. (c) state governed by small group of people 4. (a) knowledge on a subject 5. (b) cut short 6. (b) local political party committee
7. (d) eminent or wealthy man 8. (a) adherent to party or cause
9. (c) family reunion 10. (d) combined effort

Exercise 111

1. Stain 2. Flood 3. Rite 4. Doom 5. Twilight 6. Flak
7. Relation 8. Actual 9. Marriage 10. Ascetic

Exercise 112

1. aroma 2. trouble 3. keen 4. hand 5. ladle 6. tripe 7. plan
8. pickle 9. swallow 10. vapour

Exercise 113

1. August 2. Loathe 3. Authorize 4. Malign 5. Cosset
6. Mound 7. Supplement 8. Vision 9. Bant 10. Erratic

Exercise 114

1. national 2. tryst 3. comic 4. diphtheria 5. joint 6. offend
7. ecstatic 8. emerge 9. scratch 10. group

Exercise 115

1. naturalized 2. natural 3. intersect 4. ambidextrous
5. evolution 6. hamlet 7. trespassing 8. cavalier
9. impassive 10. vegetated

Exercise 116

1. A prejudice is a bias which is more difficult to dispel than a preconception, which is simply an idea formed beforehand.
2. Learning good manners is a natural part of education, while learning etiquette is an artificial exercise in learning a code of rules.

3. Binary means dual or in pairs. Tertiary means of the third order or formation.

4. To link something suggests that it is being looped together with something else; for example *to link arms* means to put the arm through another arm, like a chain. To join has more general connotations.

5. A sample is a specimen, where an example is a model.

6. A person who witnesses a crime will then testify in court to what he saw.

7. A person may be given credit for something he has merited, i.e. deserved, on account of his efforts.

8. Only clergymen preach sermons, while others lecture.

9. A reverie occurs when awake, while dreams only happen at night.

10. A memorial statue is constructed specifically in memory of someone, whereas a monument to the same person may commemorate his achievements.

Exercise 117

1. cent 2. row 3. bit 4. old 5. pass 6. etch 7. let 8. nut
9. lag 10. come

Exercise 118

1. PICK
   SICK
   SOCK
   COCK
   COOK
   COOP
   CROP
   DROP

2. ALL
   ALE
   LEA
   SEA
   SEW
   FEW

3. POOL
   POLL
   POLE
   PALE
   SALE
   SAKE
   LAKE

4. RICH
   RICK
   LICK
   LOCK
   LOOK
   BOOK
   BOOR
   POOR

5. WHY
   WAY
   SAY
   SAW
   SOW
   HOW

Exercise 119

1. The trick was very clever and bamboozled everyone.
2. The debate was filibustered and so was never finished.
3. As a schoolboy he was bumptious but now he is a modest man.
4. From your ingenuous comment I don't feel you quite understand the situation.
5. We came to a terrace with a balustrade.
6. Her swain was being very attentive.
7. The pancreas is a gland near the stomach.
8. The writing was so opaque that the meaning remained obscure.
9. His dishevelled appearance was alarming.
10. The glutton is addicted to eating.

Exercise 120

Education is about preparing children for the adult world. This means teaching children reading, writing and numeracy and teaching children how to behave towards others. This education of the heart is much more difficult than the education of basic skills. For what are the values of our society that we are to teach our children? We can no longer call ourselves a Christian society, for few people know anything about the Bible. This is the greatest problem for teachers today. Many of them are helpless when confronted by those ethical 'Why?' questions which the young are wont to spring upon their elders. The questions I mean are those such as 'Why is marriage sacred if most parents seem to be divorced?' or, 'If God is love, why does He allow human suffering to continue?' These are difficult questions to answer, and may be answered only if the person asked inhabits a world of values to which he can refer.

Exercise 121

1. Approaching him is a completely different issue.   2. I would like to shroud that part of the evening.   3. Current opinion favours the senior woman.   4. I shouldn't think people would, nowadays/today. 5. That car is ancient.   6. This is just the beginning of the problem.   7. He was always up early/at dawn.   8. She was consumed with envy/very envious indeed at his success.   9. I'm going to probe every possibility in discovering the truth.   10. At the moment I'm in a meeting.

Exercise 122

1. He frightens me.   2. She charmed all the family.   3. What strikes me is their courage.   4. The firm has constructed a model.   5. The train looped round the mountain.   6. Her remarks hurt us.   7. They regret that they must refuse.   8. I admire your work   9. The experience liberated me.   10. She tamed him into submission.

Exercise 123

Dieting is something that all young women think about, even though it is rarely necessary for them. The diet is a craze which is an obsession with achieving the perfect shape, which, in any case, is not an objective fact. Excessive concern about what you eat is an excuse for thinking excessively about yourself; in other words it is a manifestation of vanity.

But we must also consider the dieting phenomenon as peer group pressure which can dictate to someone how they should look and behave. This is the problem. Women shouldn't feel bullied by their more obsessive peers to feel obliged to eat only a few miserable number of calories per day. The pitiable thing is that so many women do suffer this pressure, through friends and fashion magazines.

Being this is a relatively modern fashion — very few women in the 1950s thought it desirable to rediscover their pre-pubescent shape. Speaking for myself, although I admit a faint dissatisfaction with my disproportionate bottom half, I would not swap my child-bearing hips for that unnaturally streamlined look.

Exercise 124

1. The story is lost in the past.   2. She bowed to convention/conformed, like her friends.   3. He kept the party going.   4. The lorry came to a halt.   5. The children were found safe and unhurt after their ordeal.   6. I'm working at it slowly but steadily.   7. Avoid clichés like death!   8. That dog is hideous.   9. He is now completely blind.   10. She kept cool/her cool.

Exercise 125

1. The music electrified him.   2. They greatly rely on him.   3. She argued with everyone.   4. The committee discussed the need to raise money.   5. We drifted from one place to the next.   6. The hostess introduced me.   7. His face expressed absolute horror.   8. The public has forgotten the painter.   9. All this physical work tires me.   10. Once again he has failed to communicate.

Exercise 126

Poetry is flourishing/thriving/alive in this country.   2. He droned on and on ceaselessly until I was sick with boredom.   3. This is something they always argue about.   4. The authorities/people in charge have forbidden that.   5. That paradise is long past.   6. Please don't take it personally/too seriously.   7. They supported us through everything.   8. He was always fantasising/daydreaming/building grandiose schemes.   9. I wish he wouldn't waver/change his mind all the time.   10. She looked charming/delightful.

Exercise 127

1. I crept away on all fours.   2. That book has inspired me to go travelling.   3. He then had to interpret in a different way.   4. You must understand other people's lives.   5. It reminded them of the past. 6. Doesn't this girl flourish, compared with last year!   7. Their affection touched him, after such a long time.   8. She dreamt about her childhood home.   9. The pressure intensified throughout the week.   10. His grasp of the facts impressed her.

Foreign words and phrases

If a good English equivalent exists of a foreign word or phrase that you want to use, then use it. Foreign words so often sound pretentious, or absurd, if used incorrectly. However, it's useful to be able to recognise foreign terms and many of these expressions now current in our language do not have appropriate English equivalents. Now that Latin and Greek are not commonly taught in schools and English people are notoriously bad linguists, it is vital to be familiar with foreign words and phrases that are a valuable part of the language.

a fortiori

Latin for *from yet firmer ground* or *with stronger reason*. It is a term from logic and is used to introduce a fact that, if already accepted as true, must then be doubly true:

They cannot raise money in a year, a fortiori not in six months.

With the exception of very formal writing, it is better to find an English equivalent for this term.

agent provocateur (plural: agents provocateurs)

French for describing a person who is employed to lead others, by pretending to be an accomplice, into acts for which they will be discovered and punished:

The terrorists were arrested after being betrayed by agents provocateurs employed by the government.

al fresco (also often alfresco)

Italian for *in the open air*. It is used only to describe eating in the open air; you do not swim al fresco or go to an alfresco theatre:

It was an al fresco dinner party in the garden.

alibi
Latin for *elsewhere*. In informal speech it has come to be used generally, but formally it is a legal term:

She denied witnessing the crime, her alibi being that she was looking after her children at home.

alma mater
Latin for *bounteous mother*. It is used by graduates to refer to the university where they studied.

amanuensis (plural: **amanuenses**)
Latin for someone who writes from dictation:

The ageing bestselling authoress now employed an amanuensis because she could no longer see well enough to write.

ambience/ambiance
This is French for *surroundings* and is useful to describe a general atmosphere:

The house had a pleasant ambiance.

amour propre
Means *self-love* or *self-esteem* in French:

His amour propre collapsed when he lost the libel case.

aplomb
A useful French word for describing certain actions that are performed in a self-possessed and spirited way:

She played a difficult piece with great aplomb.

a priori
Latin for *from the previous*. To argue a priori is to argue from assumed premises, not from experience:

I am arguing a priori, not having investigated the facts.

a propos (also often **apropos**)
French for *with reference to*. Do not use it in formal writing.

Apropos (of) what you mentioned ...

bête noire (plural: **bêtes noires**)
French for *black beast*. In English it is used to mean pet hate or a particularly disliked person:

Lucy was the bête noire of our tutorial group, whom everyone avoided.

billet-doux
French for *love letter*. It is usually used in a humorous sense:

A billet-doux was hidden under the cushion.

blasé
French for *surfeited with pleasure*, with the senses dulled as a result:

Living in Rome had made her blasé about the beauties of the city.

bona fide
Latin for *good faith, genuine*. The adjectival use is the more proper:

He was a bona fide doctor, with impeccable credentials.

bourgeois
Means *middle class* in French. It is commonly used in a deprecating sense:

Oh Mum! You are so bourgeois and conservative!

carte blanche
French for a *white paper*, used to mean a free hand or full permission:

I was given carte blanche to suggest anything I wanted.

chacun à son goût
Means in French *each man to his taste*:

'Do you like horsemeat?' he asked. 'Chacun á son goût.'

chargé d'affaires

French for a *person responsible for affairs of state abroad,* often an acting ambassador:

As a temporary measure they sent a chargé d'affaires while the ambassador was delayed.

chez

French for *at the house of.* It always takes the name of a person or persons after it:

The restaurant is called chez Pierre.

chic

A French word for *smart,* as applied to stylish clothes.

She always looked very fashionable and chic.

compos mentis

Latin for *in control of one's mind:*

I don't feel very compos mentis today.

contretemps

French for a *misunderstanding,* an *awkward mishap:*

There was a slight contretemps before I succeeded in making myself clear.

coup de foudre

The literal French meaning is *thunderbolt.* This is used to describe a sudden and unexpected event or love at first sight:

It was a coup de foudre - they were married in a week.

coup de grâce

French for *finishing stroke:*

With one coup de grâce his opponent was out of the game.

curriculum vitae

Latin for an *account of one's life.* It is often abbreviated to c.v., and is used only in job advertisements:

Applicants must send a full curriculum vitae.

de facto, de jure

In Latin, de facto means *in fact* or *in reality*. It is a legal term contrasting with the phrase de jure. A de facto leader does not rule on a legal basis, but simply because he has won his position. He may gain official status later if he becomes a de jure ruler – if his position becomes legally recognised:

The military general overthrew the president and became the de facto leader of the country.

de rigeur

The literal French meaning is *of strictness*. In English it is used, often humorously, to mean *required by convention or fashion*:

Hats are de rigeur at Ascot.

deus ex machina

Latin for *the god from the machine.* The term is taken from Greek drama, where a complicated plot would be resolved by the sudden appearance of a god. It can describe situations other than the plots of plays and films:

Aunt Ethel descended, like a deus ex machina, and order was restored.

dilettante

The Italian word for one who dabbles in the arts or sciences but does not pursue them seriously:

He was a dilettante of painting and poetry.

double entendre

French for the double meaning there might be in puns and innuendoes:

Wedding speeches are notorious for double entendres.

ennui

Describes a state of languor and boredom in French:

Ennui is a disease among rich people who have nothing to do.

entente cordiale
French for a complete and cordial understanding between two countries:

Once at war with each other, the two countries now enjoy an entente cordiale.

esprit de corps
French for a spirit of solidarity and unity with one's peers:

There was great esprit de corps amongst the protestors.

ex officio
Latin for *by virtue of his office*, in general used only to describe the position of committee members:

As the president he will be an ex officio member of all the subcommittees of the society.

faux pas
Means *false step* in French. It is usually used to describe tactless mistakes:

He didn't seem to notice his faux pas which embarrassed everyone.

graffiti
Italian for scribbling or drawings on walls:

Lavatory walls are the home of graffiti.

hors de combat
French for *out of the fight*. It is used to mean *injured* or in some way unable to do something:

I'm hors de combat; I can't play tennis with a broken leg.

infra dignitatem
Latin for *below one's dignity*. It is usually abbreviated in colloquial use to infra dig:

As a professional cricketer he considered it infra dig to play for his local village.

116

in loco parentis
Latin for *in the place of a parent*. A legal term defining the relationship of a principal to his pupils:

While her parents were abroad, the headmaster acted in loco parentis.

insouciance
French for *unconcern, carelessness*:

All his friends admired the insouciance of his unsettled life.

jeu d'esprit (plural: **jeux d'esprit**)
Means *witticism* in French:

The dinner conversation was full of jokes and jeux d'esprit.

kudos
A Greek word meaning *glory,* used in the sense of fame and prestige:

He gained great kudos after his second brilliant play.

laissez faire
French for *leave be*. The term is usually used to describe government policy when events are allowed to take their course:

Laissez faire was the government's policy for international trade.

louche
French for *ambiguous, disreputable, shifty*:

His louche behaviour made me suspicious.

memento mori
Means *reminder of death* in Latin. It was the term which described traditional death emblems:

This skull in the corner of the painting is a conventional memento mori reminding the viewer of his end.

milieu
French for *environment, setting*:

It was a perfect milieu for the play.

née
French for *born*. It is used in public notices of marriages and deaths to indicate a woman's maiden name:

Hilary Carey (née Thomas) died on Monday.

non sequitur
Latin for *it does not follow*:

This argument is a non sequitur and quite irrelevant.

nouveau riche (plural: nouveaux riches)
French for one who has recently acquired wealth and who usually displays it ostentatiously:

The wives of these nouveaux riches were encrusted with jewels.

obiter dictum
A Latin term with a legal meaning. It describes the opinion made by a judge when arguing a point or giving judgement which is without binding authority, for it is not essential to his decision. Out of a legal context it can therefore mean an incidental remark:

The comment was intended as an obiter dictum, not affecting the decision.

pace
Latin for *with all due respect* to the opinion of someone, notwithstanding the opinion of someone:

Pace the doctor's report, I am determined to continue running.

parvenu
French for an *upstart*, for someone who has newly risen into wealth, power or notice:

The press castigated this parvenu of politics.

patois
French for *regional dialect* or *jargon*:

This region has its own distinct patois.

persona grata/persona non grata
Persona grata is Latin for *a person in favour.* It usually refers to someone who is diplomatically in favour with a foreign government. Persona non grata means the opposite:

I am now persona non grata with the manager because of the embarrassment I landed him in.

pièce de résistance
French for the *principal course* or item:

The salmon en croûte was the pièce de résistance.

post mortem
Means *after death* in Latin. It refers to the medical examination of a corpse to discover the cause of death:

The relatives of the dead man are demanding a post mortem.

prima facie
Latin for *at first face,* it is used as an adjective or adverb to mean on a first impression:

This seems a prima facie reason for approaching him.

pro rata
Means *in proportion* in Latin:

The salary will be pro rata age and experience.

raison d'être
French for a *reason for existence*:

His raison d'être was making money.

rapport
Means, in French, feeling a sympathy and understanding for someone else:

There was an instant rapport between them.

savoir-faire

French for *skill, knowhow*:

She showed great savoir-faire in dealing with difficult clients.

soi-disant

French for *self-styled*:

He was a soi-disant painter who pioneered a new movement.

status quo

Means *the state in which* in Latin, used to mean as things were or are. It is a legal term used in official language:

The status quo is stable, now that the company has been bought.

tableau

French for *picture* or *sight*, used in English to mean a living picture – a representation of a picture by people in costume:

The play opened with a tableau of one of the later scenes.

tête-à-tête

Means *head to head* in French. In English usage it means an intimate conversation between two people:

I felt better after our tête-à-tête.

tour de force

French for a *feat of strength* or a distinguished performance:

The gymnastics at the show were a real tour de force.

vice versa

Latin for *the other way round*:

Come for a talk and then dinner, or vice versa.

virtuoso

Italian for an artist (originally a musician) of the highest skill:

She was a virtuoso pianist.

vis-à-vis

French for *face to face*. In English it is a rather pompous alternative to *about*:

Vis-à-vis this change, do you agree with the decision?

Guessing unfamiliar meanings

A large part of the English language is derived from ancient Greek and Latin. It is therefore easy to understand what an advantage those with a knowledge of these languages have. If you hear or read an unfamiliar word and you recognize the Greek or Latin word that it is derived from, you are much more likely to guess its meaning accurately.

If, for example, you came across the word *culpable* and didn't know for certain what it meant, the Latin scholar would tell you that it is derived from *culpa* (meaning 'fault' or 'blame'). To this Latin root has been added the suffix -able, thus making an adjective which is less ugly than 'blameable' and far more precise than 'faulty' when used in the context of attributing blame. Add the Latin prefix ex- (meaning 'from' or 'out of') to this same root word, and you get *exculpate*, 'to absolve', 'to clear from blame'.

A thorough study of root words, prefixes and suffixes will help you expand your vocabulary and also guide you to correct spelling. When you realise that 'disappear' contains the Latin prefix dis- ('the reverse of'), you'll have no reason to wonder whether to spell it with a double s! You do not necessarily have to become fluent in these dead languages; an awareness of what certain prefixes mean will help you even if you don't immediately recognize the root. Sometimes there are traps to fall into ('extradition' is not extra- but ex-tradition) and sometimes the living prefix has changed in meaning from its classical origin. When you think of the metric system, it is helpful to know that 'deca-' is the Greek for 'ten' and that 'deci-' is from the Latin 'decimus' meaning '(one) tenth' — the difference between a decalitre and a decilitre is then quite clear. The same applies to kilometre (Greek 1000) and millimetre (Latin 1000) etc.

A number of Greek and Latin prefixes follows.

GREEK AND LATIN PREFIXES

ab-   *(L) away from*
            abstract, abscond
ad-   *(L) to*
            advance, admit
ambi-   *(L) on both sides*
            ambidextrous, ambience, ambiguous
amphi-   *(G) on both sides*
            amphibious, amphitheatre
an-   *(G) not*
            anarchy
ana-   *(G) again, up, back*
            anabaptist, anabolic, anachronism, anagram
ante-   *(L) before*
            antecedent, antechapel, antediluvian
anti-   *(G) against*
            antisocial, antibiotic, antifreeze
arch-   *(G) first, chief*
            archbishop, archangel, archetype
auto-   *(G) self*
            automatic, autograph, autonomy
bene-   *(L) well*
            benefactor, benevolence
bi-   *(L) twice, double*
            biannual, bicycle, bifurcate, bilateral
bio-   *(G) life*
            biology, biography, biophysics
cent-   *(L) a hundred*
            centennial, century
centi-   *(L) one-hundredth*
            centigrade, centilitre
circum-   *(L) around, about*
            circumnavigate, circumspect, circumlocution
com-   *(L) with*
            commiserate, commit, compose
con-   *(L) with*
            contain, convene

contra-	*(L) against*
	contradict, contraband, contraception
counter-	*(L) against, contrary*
	counter-attack, counteract, counterplot
de-	*(L) down from, away*
	depose, decadent, decay, deduce, deflect
de-	*(L) indicating reversal*
	decompose, denationalize, deoxydize
deca-	*(G) ten*
	decagramme, decalogue, decathlon
deci-	*(L) one tenth*
	decimate, decimetre, decimal
demi-	*(L) half*
	demigod, demi-monde
di-	*(G) twice, double*
	disyllabic, dichotomy
dia-	*(G) through*
	diagram, diameter, diaspora
dis-	*(L) indicating reversal, apart*
	disability, disagree, disapprove, dissociate, disappear
ex-	*(L) from, out of*
	exit, excommunicate, exhale, extradition
extra-	*(L) outside, beyond*
	extraordinary, extramural, extra-marital
hemi-	*(G) half*
	hemisphere, hemiplegia
inter-	*(L) between*
	interaction, interchange, interject
intro-	*(L) into*
	introspection, introvert, introduce
mal-	*(L) bad(ly)*
	malpractice, malform, malevolent
mega-	*(G) great*
	megaphone, megalomania, megalopolis
micro-	*(G) small*
	microphone, microscope, microbe, microcosm
mis-	*(L) wrongly*
	mistake, miscalculate, miscarriage

mono-	*(G) single, alone* monologue, monosyllable, monoxide, monochrome
multi-	*(L) many* multitude, multiple, multi-national
neo-	*(G) new* neoclassical, neolithic
non-	*(L) not* nonsense, nonentity
para-	*(G) beside, beyond* paradox, paranormal, paramilitary
pent(a)-	*(G) five* pentagon, pentameter, pentathlon
per-	*(L) through, throughout* perennial, perambulate, perforate
peri-	*(G) around* perimeter, periscope, peripatetic, peripheral
poly-	*(G) many* polyhedron, polysyllable, polymer
post-	*(L) after* postpone, post-graduate
pre-	*(L) before, surpassingly* precede, precaution, pre-eminent, preposition
pro-	*(G,L) before, in front of, for* prologue, procession, pronoun, proposition
proto-	*(G) first (-formed), primitive* protoplasm, prototype, protocol
pseudo-	*(G) false* pseudonym, pseudo-science
retro-	*(L) going backwards* retrograde, retrospection
semi-	*(L) half* semicircle, semi-precious, semiquaver
sub(ter)-	*(L) below, beneath* subterfuge, subterranean, subconscious
super-	*(L) above, over* superior, superintend, superhuman
syn-	*(G) with, together, alike* synchronize, synonym, synthesis

tele-	*(G) far, distant*
	television, telemetry, telepathic, telephone
trans-	*(L) across, beyond, through*
	transfer, transatlantic, transform
ultra-	*(L) beyond*
	ultrasonic, ultraviolet, ultra-modern
vice-	*(L) in place of*
	viceroy, vice-captain

Thought for the day

A great writer visits a school in Tanganyika

'I should have known better than to put my head into that classroom. I have been caught before in this way by nuns. I smirked and attempted to get away when I heard the fateful words ".... would so much appreciate it if you gave them a little address."

' "I am awfully sorry I haven't anything prepared. There's nothing I could possibly talk about except to say how much I admire everything."

' "Mr Waugh, these boys are all wishing to write good English. Tell them how you learned to write so well."

'Like a P. G. Wodehouse hero I gazed desperately at the rows of dark, curious faces.

' "Mr Waugh is a great writer from England. He will tell you how to be great writers."

' "Well", I said, "well. I have spent fifty-four years trying to learn English and I still find I have recourse to the dictionary almost every day. English", I said, warming a little to my subject, "is incomparably the richest language in the world. There are two or three quite distinct words to express every concept and each has a subtle difference of nuance."

'This was clearly not quite what was required. Consternation was plainly written on all the faces of the aspiring clerks who had greeted me with so broad a welcome.

' "What Mr Waugh means", said the teacher, "is that English is very simple really. You will not learn all the words. You can make your meaning clear if you know a few of them."

'The students brightened a little. I left it at that.'

(*Evelyn Waugh, A Biography*; Christopher Sykes, 1975)

The advantages of Standard English over dialect

When a man speaks a language, he draws on the resources of the culture which has produced that language. He enjoys the achievements of the culture and is restricted by its limitations. Standard English is the language of English culture at its highest levels as it has developed over the last centuries: the language, not just of literature, philosophy and scholarship, but of government, science, commerce and industry. Dialects of English reflect the much more limited range of functions for which they have traditionally been used: the exchanges of everyday life, mainly among those unrefined by education. This does not mean that speakers of non-standard English cannot be verbally agile within certain areas of discourse .....

(*English our English*; John Marenbon, 1987)

The garrulous lady

"You mustn't think of going yet," said Flora — Arthur had looked at his hat, being in a ludicrous dismay, and not knowing what to do: "you could never be so unkind as to think of going, Arthur — I mean Mr Arthur — or I suppose Mr Clennam would be far more proper — but I am sure I don't know what I'm saying — without a word about the dear old days gone for ever, however when I come to think of it I dare say it would be much better not to speak of them and it's highly probable that you have some much more agreeable engagement and pray let Me be the last person in the world to interfere with it though there was a time, but I am running into nonsense again."

Was it possible that Flora could have been such a chatterer, in the days she referred to? Could there have been anything like her present disjointed volubility, in the fascinations that had captivated him?

"Indeed I have little doubt," said Flora, running on with astonishing speed, and pointing her conversation with nothing but commas, and very few of them, "that you are married to some Chinese lady, being in China so long and being in business and naturally desirous to settle and extend your connection nothing was more likely than that you should propose to a Chinese lady and nothing was more natural I am sure than that the Chinese lady should accept you and think herself very well off too, I only hope she's not a Pagodian dissenter."

(*Little Dorrit*; Charles Dickens, 1857)

Proverbs

The heart of the wise teacheth his mouth, and addeth learning to his lips.
Pleasant words are as an honey comb, sweet to the soul and health to the bones. (16: 23-24)

A fool's mouth is his destruction, and his lips are the snare of his soul. (18:7)

The English and their language

The English have no respect for their language, and will not teach their children to speak it ... It is impossible for an Englishman to open his mouth without making some other Englishman despise him.

(*Pygmalion*, Preface: G.B. Shaw, 1912)